and control
the autism friendly way

Sue Hatton
With contributions from Tracey Jones,
Alex Calver and Linda Woodcock

British Library Cataloguing in Publication Data

A CIP record for this book is available from the British Library

© BILD Publications 2016

BILD Publications is the imprint of:
British Institute of Learning Disabilities
Birmingham Research Park
97 Vincent Drive
Edgbaston
Birmingham
B15 2SQ

Telephone: 0121 415 6960
E-mail: enquiries@bild.org.uk
Website: www.bild.org.uk

ISBN 978 1 905218 42 4

BILD Publications are distributed by:
BookSource
50 Cambuslang Road
Cambuslang
Glasgow
G32 8NB

Telephone: 0845 370 0067
Fax: 0845 370 0068

For a publications catalogue with details of all BILD books and journals e-mail enquiries@bild.org.uk or visit the BILD website www.bild.org.uk/books

Printed in the UK by Latimer Trend and Company Ltd, Plymouth

People with learning disabilities and people with autism want to make their own choices and decisions about the things that affect their lives. To help make this happen, BILD works to influence policy-makers and campaigns for change, and our services can help organisations improve their service design and develop their staff to deliver great support.

Contents

Dedication

To my three beautiful grandchildren who are helping me revisit the significance of those early stages of human development and with whom I have such fun.

Reuben, Simeon and Emete.

Thank you.

Acknowledgements

It has been a privilege to work with a number of people on this book. The chapters written with Alex Calver and Tracey Jones use their real names at their request. Linda Woodcock in her chapter on the family perspective has anonymised other people she writes about, but many of you will know Linda from her own writings and hearing her speak at conferences or have had the privilege of being trained by her. All the stories I tell in the book about people with autism or their families and staff who work with them are true but they have also been anonymised to protect identity.

I am extremely fortunate to be in a job where I can develop an organisation strategically whilst still working directly with a number of individual people on the autism spectrum and their staff teams. I see it as an essential way of working to be truly effective because I know I need to keep learning. Those with autism with whom I meet regularly continue to teach me. Thank you to them and to my boss Amanda Morgan-Taylor who trusts me to get on with the job.

Foreword

It is rare to find such a clear easy-to-read text on an important topic directed specifically to those (parents and professionals) who care for and support adults on the autism spectrum. It is written by someone with a lifetime's experience of this population that includes the full spectrum from those with additional learning disabilities to those with Asperger syndrome or high functioning autism who are being supported to live as independently as possible. The book also includes chapters written by a parent and by two people on the spectrum.

But this is not just another basic guide to autism. It refers to the particular characteristics of autistic thinking and the aim is to move supporters from a state of 'autism awareness', which it assumes most practitioners have achieved, through the ability to create 'autism friendly' support and finally to achieve 'autism intelligence'. Autism intelligence is defined not just as greater understanding of autism but, perhaps more importantly, the ability to translate that understanding into day to day interactions and interventions with those they support.

This not only means better and more autism appropriate practice but also a challenge to a key shibboleth of practice in supporting adults in social care – the provision of 'choice'. Sue Hatton does not, of course, oppose providing choice but illustrates (with many practical examples) that in autism this is a very problematic concept. As she shows, it is informed choice that is needed and that cannot be assumed in autism; it needs to be specifically taught.

This is a passionate book with a simple yet profound message. It should be a feature of all training for those working with adults on the spectrum. It will be a valuable resource for all providers of such services, for parents and for those on the spectrum themselves who need to help the well-meaning but often bewildered neurotypicals who support them in providing the best support and understanding. This book has the potential to transform practice and I wish it the success it deserves.

Professor Rita Jordan PhD OBE
Emeritus Professor in Autism Studies,
University of Birmingham, UK

Choice and control the autism friendly way

Chapter 1

Why is there a need to write a book on autism and choice?

The short answer comes from the many conversations I have with support workers who work with people who have autism and an additional learning disability, including things like:

> "But it is his choice to stay in his room and we are told we have to let him make his own choices."

> "He chooses to play on his computer all the time and is just not interested in anything else, but as he is an adult, it is up to him."

> "Well, it is her house so if she wants to leave it dirty what can I do? She is an adult and has the right to make her own decisions but I agree with you it is not very nice. I always make sure I don't need the loo when I come to support her because her bathroom is disgusting."

The concept of 'choice' is rightly very important in learning disability services. However, my concern about choice being offered to people on the autism spectrum who also have a learning disability has grown and grown. I work as an autism adviser for a health and social care company and my role takes me into residential and supported living services for people with a diagnosis of autism, many of whom have an additional learning disability. It is a role that takes me the length and breadth of the UK. Prior to my current job, I worked for an autism specific charity that also ran residential and supported living services where the issues were often the same. In my experience, there are a number of common misunderstandings about choice that warrant further exploration and understanding if we are to support people with autism in truly person centred and autism friendly ways. To begin to gain an insight, let us hear what those with autism have to say about choice.

> *"I prefer to be told what is happening and where we are going to do the shopping. I find it really quite stressful when I am given a choice. People find this hard to understand but it is true – being given choice makes me feel very anxious."*

> (Tim aged 35 who has autism and learning disabilities)

How then do you approach supporting Tim? Should we take away choices as he is telling us they cause him stress? I would say yes, often this is the right thing to do because it is the autism friendly thing to do. This gets directly to the heart of the dilemma around choice in learning disability services where many people with autism are supported and also in services that are referred to as autism specific. There are a great many people with either diagnosed or undiagnosed autism in learning disability services with an estimate of one in one hundred people within England (Department of Health, 2014) in the total population. Tim is one of many people on the autism spectrum who is able to articulate the fact that he finds choice stressful. Even when support staff know this about a person they work with, they may still consider choice should be at the centre of what we refer to as a person centred way of working.

In the book by Liz Tilly on person centred approaches when supporting people with a learning disability (Tilly, 2011) there is a whole chapter on choice:

> *"This chapter is about being aware of people's rights to make their own choices and ensuring they have the opportunity to do this in large and small decisions each and every day."*

Can you begin to see how this way of working could be very frightening for someone like Tim who has said how stressful he finds choice? Being person centred for Tim means staff are going to have to learn about doing this in an autism friendly way. This may include reducing the amount of choice Tim is faced with each day and at times it may be to ensure he has no choices that need to be made on some days. This could include not offering the choice of a shower or a bath in the morning, to select his clothes for him and determine his breakfast cereal. This rightly goes against the grain in good support services today and I am not saying this would need to happen all of the time. I would hope staff could work with Tim to enable him to make a simple choice like which cereal to have most mornings. However, on the days when Tim is clearly very anxious, one way to reduce that anxiety is to not offer him any choices. On these days, the person centred thing to do is for Tim to be told to use the shower and have Weetabix for breakfast.

Many of the people I am concerned about live in or are supported by services for people with a learning disability who may not have autism. For them, choice is important and may cause no stress at all. Choice will be a valued part of their daily lives as it is for so many of us who like to be able to decide which cereal to have in a morning or to make an out of character choice and have a boiled egg.

If we are to be person centred, then we need to both understand these differences and be able to accommodate them within the support we offer. I would like to recommend the following steps to ensure that when we support people with autism and a learning disability we are able to do this. Here are the three steps I will refer to throughout this book.

Step 1 – Being autism aware

All staff working with people who have a learning disability need a basic awareness training in autism as some of those they support will also be on the autism spectrum. They may or may not have a diagnosis, but we always need to be aware. Very often you will find the word autism or 'autistic traits' or 'autistic tendencies' written in a care plan or support plan. Being aware is the first step to recognising that a person may need to be supported in a different way and especially in relation to making choices. However, that awareness may not really impact on daily support practice until the next step is taken.

Step 2 – Being autism friendly

Beyond simple awareness, we need to have an understanding of how our support practice may need to alter when we recognise that someone has autism. To be 'autism friendly' means we have some knowledge and understanding of what autism is and how it affects people. Therefore, we recognise how the support we offer should be adapted to meet the sometimes quite different needs that a person may have.

If I was supporting both Tim (who has autism) and Jack (who has a learning disability but is not on the autism spectrum) to make their breakfast in a morning, I may have to work in two quite different ways. This would be especially true if I knew that Tim had become agitated when he woke up. For Jack, I may offer a full range of cereals and remind him there were also eggs available, leaving him to make his decision about what he wanted. However, to be what I call 'autism friendly' and knowing how choice impacts on Tim, I may well get out the Weetabix and say to Tim, *"Here is your breakfast Tim"* or I might offer only two cereal choices.

Step 3 – Being autism intelligent

I actually think there is a third step to take but it is one that only comes in time, with experience and having an ongoing inquiring mind that seeks to learn more and more about autism and the very varied ways it affects people. Only then can we really begin to act and support people in 'autism intelligent' ways. This will become more apparent as you read through the book and I reveal how I still struggle to work in autism intelligent ways with all the people I currently work with. It is not something that comes naturally as my mind does not work in the same way, but it is something we can learn and in my experience we can acknowledge that we need to go on learning when we spend time with someone on the autism spectrum.

I have been challenged about my ideas many times by staff who advocate for the human rights of people with learning disabilities to make their own choices good or bad. Having the rights of any British citizen was enshrined in *Valuing People Now* (Department of Health, 2009) the three year Government strategy for people with a learning disability in England in order to ensure people are fully included in society regardless of their intellectual ability. It has been wonderful to see more people with learning disabilities fulfilling their right to vote, getting involved in politics and fighting the prejudice that sadly still exists today. The citizen advocacy and self advocacy movement started in the 1980's and 1990's that are ongoing played a vital role in ensuring that *Valuing People Now* was not just a paper exercise. Within the UK the People First Movement (www.peoplefirst.org) has done a great deal to promote the rights of those with learning disabilities to be truly included in our society.

In the mid 1980's I was very involved with the development of People First in the south west region and it was both a privilege and a learning curve to realise just how many people with a learning disability were able to speak up for themselves and let services know what they wanted and needed. Many people who had spent years in long stay institutions were gaining a voice and as they moved into local communities also wanted to make their contribution to society.

The campaigning movement from those with a learning disability supported the recognition and pressure for people with autism to lead 'fulfilling and rewarding lives' (Department of Health, 2010). Indeed the Mental Capacity Act 2005 enshrines the rights for all of us, including those with a learning disability and people with autism, to be able to make our own decisions as long as we are deemed to have capacity. Provided that the person has capacity it does not matter if they are thought to be unwise decisions, because all people have the right to make unwise choices and decisions. Something I agree with, but, it leads into the next area of concern I have with the way learning disability services can work with people with autism.

> *"It does not bother me having smelly dirty breath and I don't believe I will get toothache if I don't clean my teeth."*
>
> (Adam, aged 28, who has autism and a mild learning disability living in supported living)

You and I may think this is unwise, but Adam is deemed to have capacity in relation to this area of health care as the Mental Capacity Act states that a person is deemed to have capacity in relation to a decision when they can understand the consequences of the decision and weigh up the pros and cons of those consequences. He has had several people talk to him about dental hygiene and what may happen if he does not look after his teeth. Staff have explained to him about how it is not very pleasant for other people when Adam has bad breath and it could mean people don't really want to be friends with him. So for the staff in his support team they feel they have done their job and enabled him to make an 'informed choice.' This is something I would challenge knowing about Adam and how his autism impacts upon him.

Adam is autistic and like most people with autism lives very much in the present moment. His autism also means that he has what is known as a poor 'theory of mind' (Baron-Cohen, 1995). Our theory of mind is our ability to have insight into what other people think and feel. It is something that most children develop naturally as they grow up and among many things it gives us the ability to empathise. However, if you have autism your mind functions differently. One of those differences is that people with autism do not develop a theory of mind as early as more typically developing children and they rarely develop it to the same degree. This makes it extremely difficult for Adam to conceive what others may think and feel even when he is told as he can't really hold this image in his head or fully understand it. Consequences like toothache are in the future and once again you need to be able to imagine this, to have the picture in your head of what it might mean in order to really understand the consequences of the decision you are making. As for taking account of what other people think and feel, he does not really know how to as he can't really grasp the fact that people think differently to him, even when he has it explained. The explanation is not processed and does not make sense to Adam. What Adam can do is give the appearance that he has understood and that he is choosing to make this decision about his teeth, fully aware of all the consequences described.

Staff are autism aware, they are trying to be 'autism friendly' by carefully explaining things to Adam. In order to work well with Adam in a person centred and what I would call an autism intelligent way, further steps would need to be taken. Without quite a high level of autism knowledge and a good grasp on what theory of mind is and how it impacts on Adam the obvious outcome is exactly what currently happens. *"It is his choice."* This is getting quite complicated and for so many of the staff I meet and work with choice is simple and it is the right of all people with a learning disability with or without autism to make their own choices. I am conscious of sounding very restrictive and authoritarian and I don't really want to be seen like that. I would fight for people's rights to their own self-determination, but if we really listen to people with autism and seek to be autism intelligent we will find supporting them to really make an informed choice is time consuming and takes considerable effort on our part. I do not think it is enough to say:

> *"If he chooses not to clean his teeth and I have explained the consequences to him it is up to him, he knows what he is doing and he has the right to make these bad choices. That is what learning to be an adult is all about."*

(Member of support staff for Adam)

Is it? My concern is that we assign a level of psychological ability to people with autism who are verbal that they may not have. We think if they have been given an explanation of the consequences and still choose not to clean their teeth then it is up to them. It is their human right. However, if there was a better understanding of autism and in Adam's situation his lack of ability to imagine or visualise the consequences we are talking about, then we might work differently with him and we might get a different result. My recommendation would be certainly to accept his decision initially and then over a period of time help him to see the consequences of poor dental hygiene. Possibly take Adam to meet someone with rotten teeth and get them to talk about the pain they have and how they wish they had cleaned their teeth. Take photos of this person, get Adam to think about what he heard and write it down there and then. Keep a folder of these photos and Adam's thoughts. Try to set up a visit with a dentist or a dental nurse or hygienist and get them to talk not directly to Adam about his personal decision, but about the things they see in their job due to poor dental hygiene. Though I would not do this at the dentist surgery – much better over a cup of coffee in a café with a dental nurse that someone on the staff team happens to know or is related to. Again record what is said, pictures would be good if

Choice and control the autism friendly way

they can be provided, of the reality being spoken about. Get Adam's reactions and record these. Keep all this information in a folder so it can be looked at and reflected upon over time. The internet would be a good source of visual support but the more real and personal the information can be the better.

This way of working is time consuming, it takes thinking in a different way, what I would describe as autism friendly and autism intelligent thinking, but it is the only way to truly help someone like Adam. His verbal ability masks the considerable difficulties his autism brings and only over a period of time with good visual supports and where possible real life experiences and the support to record and reflect can you say that Adam is really able to make a choice about his teeth. This is not easy to do and it is not easy to see the need for working in this way but this level of understanding is required if we are to change the attitude of:

> "It is his choice, I am here to support him, but I can't make choices for him that would not be right, if he chooses to not clean his teeth each day all I can do is remind him that it helps to prevent tooth decay."

> (Member of support staff)

I believe to be person centred in an autism intelligent way requires so much more in relation to choice.

Perhaps one of the most challenging situations I meet and sadly a regular experience is the person who is choosing to stay in their bedroom and not engage with other people or in activities that are provided or suggested by those supporting them. I am told that choices are offered very regularly and staff try hard to suggest things they know the person has enjoyed in the past or that they think will be of interest. Once again I think the dilemma in this situation is that staff have not been trained to both think and work in an autism friendly and autism intelligent way. Very intellectually able people with autism often describe facing each day as a stressful experience. John Simpson with whom I co-wrote *Next Steps in Supporting People with Autistic Spectrum Conditions* (Hatton and Simpson, 2012) says:

> "For me each morning feels like facing an interview for a new job and this makes life hard work. Staying in bed can often be so much easier unless there is something really motivating to get up for and by that I mean motivating for me – it won't be the kinds of things most neurotypical people will be motivated by."

What of those people who are not able to tell us that they experience stress just from the experience of waking up? They are faced with a well-intentioned member of support staff enthusiastically suggesting they could go swimming today or for a walk to the sea. Are these activities real motivators for someone like Joe who spends a great deal of time rocking and twiddling pieces of thread he tears from his clothing in order to reduce his stress?

There are thousands of excellent support staff up and down the country. They know some of the people they support have autism because they have read their support plans carefully and all additional paper work. They are autism aware. They may well have completed an e-learning module on autism and a one-day face to face training session. It can be very demoralising for staff who are genuinely trying hard to care and support in the right way using all their ingenuity to encourage Joe out of bed by offering a range of activities that they know Joe can and does enjoy. Facing the stressful experience of a new day may go so much better with very little spoken language and careful consideration given to John Simpson's question:

"What's in it for me?"

John tells us how hard he finds it to be motivated by things that motivate most neurotypical people and how he needs to be able to see a motivator for him if he is going to get up and face the stress of a new day.

If we can't think of why our suggestions might not be motivational for Joe maybe we need to think again. If Joe is a person who spends time twiddling pieces of thread perhaps if we sat on the bedroom floor with a piece of material and pulled threads and twiddled, seeking to be autism friendly, we might find that Joe wants to get up and engage with us in a ten minute twiddling session to start his day. This could then lead into silently getting on with his morning routine. A simple, clear routine that all staff follow to ease Joe into his day, in an autism friendly way. This would be referred to as an 'intensive interaction' way of working advocated by Dave Hewett et al (Hewett et al, 2011) and Phoebe Caldwell (Caldwell, 2005). A way of seeing the world and indeed sensing the world from Joe's viewpoint. Intensive interaction is a very autism intelligent approach and especially helpful for staff working with people on the autism spectrum who have an additional severe learning disability. A joint twiddling session may be the best motivator for Joe and a great, if unusual way to start his day. Phoebe Caldwell has produced a number of really helpful DVDs where you see her demonstrating this autism friendly way of working (Caldwell, 2007 and 2010).

"But I can't really call that work can I? Sat down twiddling a bit of thread? I am here to support Joe to have a fulfilling and rewarding life."

(Member of support staff)

It is not that I believe twiddling thread is a totally fulfilling and rewarding life for Joe and of course I would want Joe to have more in his life that he does find enjoyable. But, with what I am describing as an autism friendly and autism intelligent approach to the concept of choice, I do think more staff could and should feel that sitting still and twiddling is really work.

There are some occasions when I believe we need to reduce the choices offered to a person with autism or give no choice. Just before I do that I want to assure you that ultimately I do think people with autism can make choices. Later in the book I will begin to outline the ways we can and should be enabling people to understand choice, to be able to weigh up different choices and to select what they believe will be best for them having fully understood the consequences of the choices made. Though I warn you it means for those of us working with and supporting people with autism that we have work to do and there are no easy or quick solutions. I am very aware this goes against the grain and want to turn to some historical sources to understand why the emphasis on choice has become so important when working with people with learning disabilities. There is lots we can do to support people to move forward and make their own choices but to be truly effective we need to take steps from autism awareness to autism friendly ways of working and as far as possible to learn to stop and think in autism intelligent ways if we are to make choice meaningful for those with autism we support. Next we will take a look back in time to see how we have got to this situation over choice for people with autism. Once we have explored the historical context more and heard from those on the autism spectrum and some family members we will return to how to take those steps towards autism intelligence with lots of real life and current examples of staff working successfully in this way.

Choice and control the autism friendly way

Chapter 2

How and why choice became so important

Just over one hundred years ago the Mental Deficiency Act of 1913 introduced compulsory admissions to large long stay institutions for those who were deemed to be 'mentally defective'. This label covered a wide range of people including those with learning disabilities and autism.

> "The aim of the services was to segregate people who were seen
> as different or a nuisance from the rest of society by placing them
> in large institutions in rural areas, to isolate males and females
> and to protect society from people who were seen as dangerous
> and unacceptable. This led to the building of massive custodial
> warehouses which were designed to control rather than cure."
>
> (Sperlinger, 1992)

It was in the 1960's and 1970's that attitudes and practice really began to alter and this was in part down to the concept of 'social role valorisation' and the work of a man called Wolf Wolfensberger (Wolfensberger, 2004) who challenged the idea that because people with a learning disability (then referred to as mentally retarded or subnormal) were different, did not make them of less value as people. He was building on the concept of 'normalisation' that held that *"all people with learning disabilities, irrespective of their age or disability have the same human rights as non-handicapped people"* (Sperlinger, 1992).

This movement spread from Scandinavia to America, Canada and Britain as well as to other parts of Europe. It led to a major change in our educational law in 1970 (The Education (Handicapped Children) Act 1970) when it was legislated that all children regardless of how severe their disability should receive an education. This was quickly followed by the 1971 White Paper, *Better Services for the Mentally Handicapped* (Department of Health, 1971) which paved the way for further change to improve the lives of those with a learning disability, many of whom had autism.

> *"The 1971 White Paper set an agenda for the next two decades which focused on reducing the number of places in hospitals and increasing the numbers in the community. It committed the government to helping people with learning disabilities to live as 'normal a life' as possible, without unnecessary segregation from the community. It emphasised the importance of close collaboration between health, social services and other local agencies."*
>
> (Valuing People, 2001)

I myself was part of these changes in both legislation and attitude. In 1973 I was a student on one of the few teacher training courses in the country at the time to train people to teach children who were referred to as 'educationally subnormal'. My first teaching practice was on a children's ward in a large long stay institution and my teaching certificate states that though I am also trained for primary education my main subject rather than English or Maths or History was 'subnormality'. When I refer to this with staff teams in training sessions today I usually find I need to remind them that I am not a hundred and ten years old. It is only since 1970 that children with what we now refer to as a severe learning disability have had a right to an education and teachers needed to be specially trained for the work. Initially many of my lectures at college came from psychiatrists and nurses who worked at the nearby long stay subnormality hospital. It was here I first learnt about autism, but very much based on the work of Leo Kanner (Kanner, 1943). Kanner wrote about autism associated with severe learning disability.

Personal choice was almost non-existent in these institutions, residents lived on wards with those they were put with. They shared clothes, ate what was provided and were not involved in any decisions that affected their lives (Brown and Smith, 1992). It was against this backdrop that the push for the right to 'an ordinary life' really began as an initiative promoted in a book of the same name (King's Fund Centre, 1980) and followed by *An Ordinary Life in Practice* (Towell, 1988). The authors who contributed to these significant publications wanted to make explicit the following fundamental principles:

> *"1.   People with learning disabilities have the same human value as anyone else and the same human rights.*
>
> 2.   *Living like others within the community is both a right and a need.*
>
> 3.   *Services must recognise the individuality of people with learning disabilities."*

The focus on choice was central to these books and to the work of John O'Brien (O'Brien and Lyle O'Brien, 1988). O'Brien's five accomplishments of normalisation set out key principles related to improving the quality of the lives of people with learning disabilities.

1. **Community Presence** – the right to take part in community life, and to live and spend leisure time with other members of the community

2. **Relationships** – the right to experience valued relationships with non-disabled people

3. **Choice** – the right to make choices, both large and small. These include choices on where to live and with whom to live

4. **Competence** – the right to learn new skills and participate in meaningful activities with whatever assistance is required

5. **Respect** – the right to be valued and not treated as a second class citizen

This work has been tremendously important in altering and improving the lives of thousands of people with learning disabilities. Though not everything was terrible in the long stay institutions. I worked in one in the mid-80s as it was facing closure, people were very much second class citizens and both attitudes and practice at times were quite simply wrong. During 1986 I ran an adult education class for people with learning disabilities living mainly in one particular long stay institution in the Bristol area and the class was about advocacy and learning to speak up for yourself. The group produced a small booklet about themselves, their lives in the institution and their hopes for the future. I got into trouble with the senior staff at the hospital for encouraging 'patients' to cause trouble on their wards by teaching them that they had rights. This is hard to believe now but I still have a copy of the booklet that was banned and I was told, could not be circulated. 1986 is not so very long ago. Then I would certainly have echoed John O'Brien and many others who were stressing the significance of choice. People had been denied choice for too long, change was happening and thank goodness it was. But in 1986 I did not understand much about autism, despite it being part of my curriculum at teacher training college. You could say I was 'autism aware' but that was as far as it went. That began to change over the following 20 years as I got to know more people with autism and as I began to really learn more about what it is to have autism and the considerable stress trying to live an 'ordinary life' is for people with autism.

Choice was becoming a watch word for all forward thinking practitioners in the field of learning disabilities and when the Department of Health for England published the White Paper, *Valuing People* in 2001 (Department of Health, 2001) it was only fitting to have a whole section dedicated to 'choice and control' for people with learning disabilities. The policy objective was stated in the following way:

> *"To enable people with learning disabilities to have as much choice and control as possible over their lives through advocacy and a person-centred approach to planning the services and support they need."*

The policy promoted truly person centred ways of planning and delivering services and support. To do this it was and still is felt that the person with learning disabilities needs to be at the centre of that plan, their wishes, aspirations, their needs should be adhered to. A way of working that in so many ways should be applauded and when I think of the restrictive practices I witnessed in the 1970s I know we have come a long way and it is a journey that was vital if the lives of people with learning disabilities were to be truly valued. But I believe it is a journey that has not paid sufficient attention to the needs of people with a learning disability and autism. Of course the rights of people with autism need to be promoted and protected but care needs to be taken when offering choice to people with autism that it doesn't result in additional stress and anxiety.

Valuing People Now followed in 2009 (Department of Health, 2009) and set out the Department of Health strategy for England making the vision of *Valuing People* a reality for all those with a learning disability. Don't get me wrong – these two papers were crucial in altering mind sets. I firmly believe in a person centred approach, where those who are supporting someone, whether they are family or paid support, really do focus on the wishes and aspirations of the person in order to improve and enhance their life experience and sense of self-worth. It is just I also firmly believe that if you are supporting someone with autism, who also has the diagnosis of a learning disability, meeting their needs actually requires you to learn to think differently. Being autism aware is not enough, being autism friendly really helps, but we need to work at ensuring that staff are what I have referred to as autism intelligent, if we are going to be able to be truly person centred and meet their very individual needs. How I believe we can learn to take these steps in good autism practice will be explored fully in the final chapter of this book.

Tom Boughton at the beginning of *An Introduction to Supporting People with Autistic Spectrum Conditions* (Hatton and Boughton, 2011) states:

> *"People need to understand MY autism if they are going to support me."*

I have known Tom a long time, but a few months ago when he was staying with me for a weekend I did not meet his needs very well and this was precisely because I tried to give him choice and what I actually did was cause him stress and anxiety – it was unintentional, but it's what I did and I am supposed to understand autism. The problem is that to think in autism friendly ways and behave with autism intelligence does not come naturally to someone like me with a neurotypical brain. So what did I do?

We were due to go shopping as Tom really enjoys looking round shops. He had requested to go to Bath and previously we have also been to Weston Super Mare and a more local shopping mall in Bristol. I was happy to go to Bath but slightly concerned about the weather as there is not so much shelter in Bath compared to the other two shopping centres mentioned. So I suggested to Tom that we should see what the weather is like in the morning and then decide which place to go to. I was thinking in a very neurotypical way. At the time Tom found it difficult to tell me, but eventually he did manage to explain that the uncertainty of not knowing which shopping centre we were going to had caused him considerable anxiety. He said he did not mind where we went, though he would like to go to Bath at some point, but the uncertainty was a stressful experience he could have done without. So what should I have done? I believe I should either have just gone to Bath regardless of the weather or I should have made the decision that it was too wet to walk round Bath and told Tom I had decided we would go to Weston Super Mare again, giving him the reason. Tom assures me this would have been much more helpful to him and would have considerably reduced his stress. However, I also think it is important that he got to visit Bath at some point so don't take my line of thinking to the extreme – that is not autism intelligent either. You may be interested to know that on Tom's next visit we agreed in advance that regardless of the weather we would visit the shops in Bath, and we did.

I am saying we need to understand the quite considerable negative impact having choice can bring for people with autism and so we need to work more intelligently to support them with the concept of choice. It is not about never giving people choice. Earlier I said that the uncertainty of not knowing which shops we were going to had caused considerable anxiety for Tom and in the next chapter we explore why choice and uncertainty can be stressful for people with autism.

Chapter 3

Why can choice cause stress and anxiety?

Choice impacts on so many areas of our lives every day:

- what time to get up
- what to wear
- what to eat and drink
- who to spend time with
- what to buy when shopping
- which mode of transport to use
- where to sit on the bus or train
- who to speak to
- when to go to the toilet
- why we need to answer a question and how to answer it

The list is endless and endless each day of our lives as we make choice after choice. To do this we need certain knowledge and much of what we require is social knowledge. If we are going to really understand why choice is so difficult for people with autism we have to first have a good knowledge and understanding of autism. We then have to be able to apply that knowledge to each person we work with so that we can gain a good insight into their autism and the way it affects them. Once we have achieved this we will be so much more aware of the acute anxiety that choice can bring to people with autism and this is what will make us work in more autism friendly and autism intelligent ways.

Let us consider some of those core difficulties and differences that people with autism experience that in turn really affect their ability to deal with choice making. We need to do this or as Dr Glenys Jones said:

> "Without this understanding, it is likely we will come to the wrong conclusions and therefore respond inappropriately and design strategies that will not work"

(Dr Glenys Jones speaking at an event on World Autism Day in Liverpool, April 2015)

We will look at six key areas of difficulty and difference for people on the autism spectrum. I use the phrase 'difficulty and difference' because there are elements to a diagnosis of autism that can and do cause considerable difficulty and particularly in relation to coping in a social world. However, it is also important for us to remember that these are differences that also offer great gifts and abilities. Danny Beath, an award winning photographer who had a diagnosis of Asperger Syndrome, said to me once when he was giving a talk in the Midlands:

> "The main reason I am so good at photography is down to my Asperger Syndrome. When I am interested in a possible photo I am happy to lie on the floor of the rain forest for five hours to wait for the moment the poisonous tree frog is in just the right position with the right light, not many neurotypical people have that skill."

Sadly Danny died of a heart attack in 2013 but his amazing photography can still be seen online at www.flickr.com/photos/flickering_velvet

Having autism brings its challenges and the focus of this book is on one of those challenges and if we understood it better we would be more able to support people with autism, but it is not all problematic all of the time as Danny so ably points out.

The six areas I am exploring are:

1. Being able to think and behave flexibly

2. Social and emotional understanding of self and others

3. Communication and language

4. The sensory experience of the world

5. The ability to shift attention

6. Experience of stress and anxiety

1. Being able to think and behave flexibly

This area of difficulty and difference was clearly identified by Lorna Wing when she first chose the phrase 'triad of impairments' that formed the basis of diagnostic criteria for autism for many years and remains central to receiving a diagnosis. It was reiterated and expanded upon in her updated edition of her original book (Wing, 2002). Initially the phrase 'impairment of the imagination' (part of the triad of impairments) was used to cover quite a wide range of difficulties that includes repetitiveness in speech and activities as well as ways of thinking.

It is as if someone on the autism spectrum is not able to easily imagine what is going to happen if the planned activity is cancelled or postponed. So routines and rituals become very important, because they are a predictable plan that can be followed. Being spontaneous, offering something new to eat for breakfast because it looked interesting is never likely to be the choice of someone on the autism spectrum, but it may be our choice and we may think it is a good idea, when it isn't.

We also talk about 'mindblindness' or 'theory of mind' in autism (Baron-Cohen, 1995) which is about the lack of ability to know what goes on in other people's heads. This requires being able to think flexibly and it is not how the brains of people with autism work. They may appear stubborn and self-centred and this is really not the case, they just cannot easily think in a different pattern to the one that is in their mind.

 This is why persuasion and argument are often not much use in your toolbox when working with people with autism. Often we find ourselves trying to get the person with autism to 'see reason' or 'see sense' when the very way their brain functions makes seeing things from anyone else's point of view other than their own almost impossible. An extremely hard thing for us with more neurotypical brains who can be persuaded, often quite easily, to change our minds or to at least understand someone else's ideas.

This reality for those on the autism spectrum can manifest itself in some challenging ways, but if we understand the need for sameness and routine we will understand the behaviour so much better and if we understand the behaviour the way we seek to work with someone will really improve.

In my work as an autism adviser I am often asked to help in situations where someone has started smearing their faeces rather than using the toilet. Quite understandably staff find this difficult to deal with. What I often discover is that there have been changes in routine. The person may have moved house, staff may have changed, the toilet may have been redecorated. People with autism often have a deep need to create a predictable pattern to feel ok and if you don't have much control over your own life then bodily functions are the one thing you can control. Smearing of faeces usually leads to the predictable pattern of being told or asked not to do it, being involved in clearing it up, having a bath and changing clothes – a lovely predictable pattern that makes the person feel so much better. But if we have not understood this and worked out what has caused the increase in anxiety and therefore the need for greater predictability, it is a pattern that is likely to continue. People on the autism spectrum love patterns, want them and actually need them.

The way people with autism think and behave, preferring to stick to rules and routines, can and does lead to many difficulties. Unlike those of us with more neurotypical brains, they are unable to work out those million and one exceptions to a rule or make changes according to external circumstances, for them a change of plan causes anxiety levels to rise. When this occurs the need for predictability increases.

Some years ago when I was working in further education, I received an urgent phone call to go to the principal's office where one of the students with autism I had responsibility for was causing a disturbance. It was the start of a new term and Nick was a young man attending a photography lesson. The tutor had finished ten minutes early and instead of being delighted like the rest of the 16- and 17-year-olds in the group, he complained to the tutor who dismissed him with a joke while the other students were telling him to be quiet. Nick then went to report the tutor to the principal. When I arrived he was giving the principal a lecture on the importance of sticking to the timetable!

Was Nick being rude and causing trouble just to get attention? No, but of course that was the conclusion most people came to. Nick found it hard to comprehend why a tutor for a course, with a lesson that was timetabled to end at 4pm, could just pack up early and go, sending the class home. No one, including and perhaps especially me, had bothered to help Nick understand how things work in further education compared to a school setting where the rules and routine were different. Something that most 17-year-olds knew well before they arrived and took full advantage of during their time at college.

Ahmed, who comes from a totally different setting, has experienced similar difficulties. Amhed lives in a residential care home for people with learning disabilities. He has autism and very little language but is quite able to dress himself in a morning. Throughout the winter months Amhed has been wearing one of his woollen jumpers to ensure he keeps warm. On this particular day the weather is quite mild so the staff member working with him says, *"You are going to be hot in that, go and change and put that jumper away. The sun is shining."*

Amhed goes back upstairs not really understanding what has been said or why, but grasps that it is something about changing his jumper. That's ok as he has a selection of five jumpers he has been wearing throughout the winter so he changes into one of the other jumpers only to be told, *"No, no jumper today, it's hot."* Confused, anxious and feeling very uncomfortable, Ahmed reluctantly takes the jumper off. Now both Amhed and the staff member are upset and frustrated. The day has not got off to a good start and it continues like this, but who is to blame?

The two situations described above are real and both caused frustration to the staff working with each of the two people – they caused frustration due to the lack of understanding of autism on the part of those paid members of staff. Perhaps more importantly though the actual behaviour of the two staff, a) ending a lesson early and b) just saying "No jumper today, it's hot" led to an increase in anxiety for those two people with autism. But unless staff are supported to understand the nature of autism and the significant need for predictability then they have not been given the tools to work with, so this is not about blaming staff, but it is a plea for better understanding in order to develop more autism friendly practice.

I will finish this section by saying that of course changes do happen and we need to do our best to help people with autism cope with change. This can be done with good planning and preparation.

Remember:

- People with autism have a need for routines and rituals
- Flexible plans and changes in plans are not easy for people with autism
- Staff should always consider how to prepare a person for changes that will take place wherever possible
- Help to maintain and keep to the plan and routine wherever possible

2. Social and emotional understanding of self and others

When you first learn about autism hopefully one of the things explained to you is the rather spikey or uneven profile that someone on the spectrum has. There are things that they are really good at that will surprise you and things that they really struggle with that can also surprise you (Hatton and Simpson, 2012). In particular, social and emotional understanding is a challenge for people with autism, understanding their own emotions and feelings as well as those of other people. Grasping how social relationships work is at the heart of the challenges people with autism face in a very social world. Wendy Lawson (Lawson, 1998) in her book, *Life Behind Glass* says:

> *"For me, the ordinary interactions of my daily social experiences have always been a great mystery."*

> *"I find emotions interchangeable and confusing. Growing up, I was not able to distinguish between anger, fear, anxiety, frustration and disappointment."*

I think this is really hard for so many of us to understand as we develop our own social knowledge so naturally and instinctively. Also, as a very small child, we may explode with anger if we are not allowed a second chocolate biscuit but we soon learn to ask nicely or accept the refusal with minor disappointment. These are indications that both our emotional understanding and control is developing and with it a quite sophisticated knowledge of how we ourselves work and how other people function in relation to us. Such a different experience for Wendy Lawson, as she describes above. It is the area in autism that can lead to real vulnerability both growing up and in adulthood. Staff need to be equipped to really help those with autism they support to both understand themselves better and what friendships and relationships are and how they work.

During staff training I try to give as many examples as possible in relation to this area for people with autism as it is so difficult for neurotypical people to understand. Teaching social and emotional skills and knowledge are extremely challenging because they are so nuanced.

Consider standing at a bus stop waiting for a bus. Someone else joins you at the stop. Do you acknowledge them? Do you speak to them? If they say something to you do you respond? Do you respond in a very brief way, seeking to close the conversation that has yet to really start or do you answer in a way that invites extending the conversation?

The answer to all those questions is, 'it depends.' It depends on how you are feeling. It depends on what they say and the way they say it. It depends on what the other person looks like. It depends on the weather (we are far more likely to enter into casual conversations in more extreme weather conditions – the weather being such a popular topic of conversation in the UK). I have spent a long cold evening in a waiting room at a station hoping for a train as the roads were frozen and all the buses cancelled. The small group of us in that waiting room became quite well acquainted during those hours, an experience I had no idea was going to happen and could not have prepared for, but I coped.

So much of the way we are, socially and emotionally, depends on circumstances at the time and with a more neurotypical brain we can adapt and deal with a wide variety of circumstances making choices and decisions according to the situation as we go along. For people with autism, it is so very different and their response at the bus stop may lead them into confusion, being misconstrued or even put them in danger.

Rebekah has autism and travels to and from college independently. She has been taught by her parents not to talk to strangers and heard this phrase repeated by others and she always ensures she sticks to this rule. She is going in a little later to college and the bus stop is quiet, only one other older lady standing with her who asks, *"What are you up to today then?"* Rebekah just ignores her and waits for her bus, which eventually comes, and they both get on the same bus. Rebekah goes upstairs as she likes to be able to look down on the streets and houses. At the next stop someone else gets on and comes upstairs, there is no one else on the upper deck except for Rebekah. It happens to be a tutor at the college Rebekah attends and though she does not teach Rebekah she recognises her and smiles and says *"Hello, off to the same place as me are you? "* Once again Rebekah, who does not recognise the tutor out of the context of the college, carried on looking out of the window and ignores the woman who spoke. This 15 minute experience leaves one person thinking Rebekah is plain rude and the other thinking she is deaf – both of which are common responses to people with autism.

A very different experience in a similar situation happened to Michelle. Michelle has been learning in her social skills course about friendship, how you make friends and what it is to be a friend. She knows that a smile is an important first step and so is delighted when the man standing at the bus stop smiles at her. He begins to chat and she feels quite happy about this because he smiled and she knows that is a first step to friendship. Within seven minutes she has given the man the five pound note she has in her purse for her lunch and gets on the bus feeling very pleased that she now has a friend and in fact a boyfriend. How she will pay for her lunch does not occur to her, why he wanted the money and if she will ever see him again does not enter her head. When she arrives at college she is keen to inform her social skills tutor that she now has a boyfriend and things only go wrong in Michelle's eyes when it gets to lunch time.

Both of those stories are true and if you are working with people with autism who are using public transport independently they are situations that need careful consideration and a large amount of work to be able to deal with them. Telling someone not to speak to strangers is of no help as we all speak to strangers and there are times when we really need to. Equally a smile from someone does not make them your friend, but it does indicate something and that something is what we with neurotypical brains are so good at interpreting and those with autism are not.

I always feel when I am talking about what people with autism can't do, it is also important to remember the gifts and skills they have. The person with autism at the bus stop may be incapable of interpreting a smile from a stranger but they are quite likely to know the exact time the next bus is due and the type of bus it will be. I was once stuck in Birmingham as the trains had been cancelled and I had no idea about how to get a bus back home, but I knew who would, a young man with autism. I rang him and he kindly directed me to the correct bus stop, gave me the number of the bus and told me when it would next be along and where to get off as I neared home. Valuing and using the skills that autism brings will be important when we begin to look at how to help people with the complexities choice brings.

Remember:

- If the person with autism you support wants to have friends and relationships, helping them to become more self-aware is a good place to start

- Supporting them to have some insight into their own autism can also be very beneficial

- Give people opportunities to practice social skills through role play and also in real situations

3. Communication and language

There are people with autism who do not use any spoken language but of course they can and do communicate with us. Then there are those people with autism who speak a great deal, but their ability to actually communicate with us is quite limited.

Donald who has autism, learning disabilities and is non-verbal is very clear in communicating the fact that he wants a cup of tea as he heads regularly for the kitchen searching for a mug and a teabag. Yet Carl who lives in the same home and talks all the time about football, how many goals Manchester United scored in their last game, who scored them, who they are playing next and what the likely outcome of that match will be, needs encouraging to have a drink as he does not appear to know his body needs the liquid.

So often we make the wrong assumptions about people with autism based mainly on their ability to speak. Those with no speech or very few spoken words are often thought not to be able to express their needs (though Donald described above certainly does) or understand what is being said around them. Having no verbal language is not necessarily a sign of poor understanding and an inability to communicate what is wanted and needed. Phoebe Caldwell (Caldwell, 2010) in her book on intensive interaction talks about 'learning the language' of people with autism who are non-verbal because they certainly do communicate.

I was recently working with a young man called Christopher who talks a very great deal. He talks about the TV programmes he watches and also about activities he enjoys but has not taken part in for several months. When offered an activity staff say he has enjoyed in the past, though he says he is going to go, at the last minute he changes his mind. They interpret this as being his choice. Christopher's ability to speak and use language does not mean he understands things said to him. Rather he has developed a routine and a pattern of talking and talking, saying yes he will go out and then saying no he won't, none of which has much to do with what he really wants to do. It is a pattern, a very predictable pattern in which staff play their part with their suggestions of an activity, offering the activity and then saying how disappointed they are that he has chosen not to go this time. It could almost be acted out in a foreign language for all the real meaning there is to the actual words, but the predictable pattern is needed by Christopher and it is going to take some hard work to support him to try a different pattern. Hard work worth doing as I believe he would really enjoy and benefit from going to the weekly swimming session. We just need to find a way of motivating him enough to create a new pattern.

It is vital to have a good understanding of the communication and language issues in autism if you are to work with people with autism. First it is important to grasp that having language does not mean the person can communicate well or understand well. By the same token, having no language does not mean the person is unable to communicate or understand. This is confusing. I find it confusing, so it is not surprising that the many staff I meet during training sessions on autism are also confused. If someone speaks, surely they understand? The answer to that is, not necessarily when it comes to having autism. So in relation to staff offering choices, Christopher does not get to go out much at the moment. Though with a more autism friendly and autism intelligent approach I believe he will join in activities regularly and enjoy them. Similarly Daniel who lives in the same house but has almost no language does swim regularly each week and he enjoys it. However, he never gets to go to football because it is thought he would not understand the game. I think he might understand more than we imagine and I want to encourage him to have the opportunity to surprise us.

The staff working with Christopher and Daniel are good, but they do need to learn more about autism and the way it impacts on people. The service they work in is for people with learning disabilities who have autism written on their personal information file but it has not got on to their care plan or person centred plan. There is no awareness of the central need to understand autism for these two men and to understand how it impacts differently for each of them, especially in relation to the use of language and the ability to communicate. Sadly, wrong assumptions have been made based on the verbal ability of these two men. This has led to assumptions about their level of understanding that are not very accurate. Both Christopher and Daniel have ended up with what I would describe as a negative but predictable pattern that could do with changing to support their ongoing development and flourishing.

The staff supporting Christopher and Daniel now have a real challenge ahead to try and think in more autism friendly and autism intelligent ways to help these two men get more enjoyment in life. Creatively, a member of staff does not attempt to persuade Christopher and say how she hopes this week he will join in going swimming as this is something they know he has enjoyed in the past. What she does is go to him as the others are getting on the vehicle and say, *"I don't know if you could help me today Christopher but there is no one to help get the drinks from the café after swimming and I could do with the help. I thought you could take care of the money and get them from the café as we are getting out of the pool."* Christopher gets up and onto the vehicle and sits next to the staff member, for a while checking what drinks he has to buy and how much they will be. On arrival at the pool she says, *"If you fancy a short swim before you get the drinks I have your things here."* Christopher takes his swimming things and gets changed, he has a great time in the water but gets out in time to order the drinks for everyone from the café.

The following week may need more creative thinking but on this day Christopher had a great time. Possibly all those weeks he spent not going were not really about him choosing not to go but about the approach taken and about understanding autism and how language can often mask real comprehension.

As for Daniel, it might be surprising how much he grasps of the game of football if given the opportunity. He may not know how to choose football because he does not know what it is, but perhaps on the way back from swimming one day staff could stop to collect another resident called Jack from football and arrive early so that Daniel could get to see and experience an alternative activity. Don't take the swimming away as we know he loves that, but give him an opportunity in a more subtle way so he can both see and experience an activity that may just surprise people – and it does. The drop in to collect Jack early leads to Daniel joining in the last few minutes of the game and to the surprise of everyone when given a blue band he seems to grasp which team he is on and kicks the ball in the right direction. Before long Daniel has football added to his activity planner and soon becomes a valued member of the group.

Remember:

- Don't make assumptions about how the level of language equates to either the ability to communicate or the ability to understand

- Some people with autism who talk a great deal really struggle to tell you what they feel and also struggle to understand much of what may be said to them

- People with autism who do not speak at all can and do communicate. They may also understand more about what you say than you realise

- Don't make assumptions – get to know the person and get to know how their autism impacts upon them

---

4. The sensory experience of the world

It is only in the last two years that sensory issues for people with autism have become acknowledged as part of the diagnostic criteria. It has been very much able people on the spectrum sharing their sensory experiences in writing and public speaking that have caused this huge shift in awareness. The animated film *A is for Autism* (Webb, 1992) highlighted how the sensory perception of many people with autism works differently but it has taken a long time for diagnostic criteria to catch up with this knowledge. If noise is a problem for you then you are very likely to choose to be somewhere that is quieter even if the thing you love to do is in the noisy room. So you may appear to choose the painting activity in the quiet room but really you would like to join in the exercise class with quieter music. Compound that with the communication issues you have as a person with autism and choice becomes not only complex, but anxiety making.

For people with autism this kind of issue can be true for each of the senses, sight, taste, touch, etc. Unless we have some idea of the way each person we work with senses the world and the impact their sensory experiences have on them, we will not be able to support them in an autism friendly way.

Joe loves being involved in preparing the evening meal but recently has refused to take part. He is non-verbal and not able to explain. Maybe he has just got fed up with it, but staff don't think this is the case as he seems to want to go in the kitchen when it is time to prepare the evening meal, but then at the last minute pulls away and sits down outside. Staff begin to question whether this is his choice or whether something else is influencing his behaviour. They realise that the kitchen has recently been redecorated and the walls are now a bright yellow. Visually Joe finds this very uncomfortable and so, although he wants to be in the kitchen preparing the food, it actually hurts his eyes and he can't cope so he sits down nearby. This is not really Joe making a choice about food preparation, rather it is about sensory overload.

With a good autism profile drawn up for someone on the autism spectrum their sensory processing abilities and difficulties would be recorded for staff to work with. For Joe his profile did eventually record the difficulties he has with some colours (especially red and yellow). It also led to the kitchen being redecorated again, only this time colours were checked with all those who use the kitchen and an apple green was finally selected. If autism is just a word written in a file with little account being taken of it, you cannot expect staff to be looking out for sensory difficulties quite apart from trying to address them.

Choice and control the autism friendly way

I have been working with an autism profile for a number of years and in many ways the most important thing it does is keep the autism in mind. This is true for the staff and sometimes also for the person who has autism, if they have been able to be involved with the creation of their own profile. The following example shows the kind of information that can be recorded on a basic autism profile. Because of the visual format many people on the autism spectrum I work with have been involved in developing and therefore really owning their own profile. One such person is Malcolm who worked with his staff team to create an autism profile about himself. It is a live tool that needs to be reviewed and amended as time goes on – things will alter and develop but I find it really helps to keep the autism in mind, something I wrote about in an article for the *Good Autism Practice* journal (Hatton, 2015).

Name: Malcolm

Photograph
of the person

The uneven developmental profile or developing unevenly

People with autism have an uneven profile of development. They surprise us with the amazing things they can do and also the things they struggle with.

Some key strengths:

Malcolm has an amazing memory – remembering details from years ago, as if it was yesterday.

He is very sociable – enjoys the company of others and likes contributing to what is going on around him.

He also has a really strong desire to learn new things, whether it be facts about a particular area or a new recipe. He follows instructions well (ie recipes).

He knows a great deal about a number of topics. Public transport is the main topic he is knowledgeable about.

Some key struggles:

Malcolm struggles with change, especially with changes in support staff.

He also wants people to know that even changes in staff appearance can be difficult for him.

He is uncomfortable around dogs – he finds them very unpredictable.

The image of a jigsaw is often used to help us understand autism, because we have some pieces of that jigsaw but not all of them. The two pieces to be completed below are about:

1. Communication and social issues

2. The need for predictability and patterns in order to feel calm

Communication and social issues

Malcolm is very sociable, but he can find it hard if he feels people are not taking any notice of him. He can also find it difficult to express his feelings. Malcolm talks well and has good language, but not when it comes to expressing what he feels about things. He does not always understand all the things that are said to him.

Patterns and predictability

Malcolm loves his daily and weekly routines. They help him feel calm and happy. Even the small details of his getting up routine need to be maintained to ensure he has a good day.

He enjoys the predictability of travelling on the bus, getting on and off at certain stops and other favourite stops.

Staff changes are very difficult for Malcolm and need careful preparation.

Important things to know and do.

Sense of seeing	Malcolm has good eyesight – a real eye for detail and he will notice when you have altered something about your appearance.
Sense of hearing	Very good hearing – even when people are talking in a different room Malcolm may come and join in the conversation as he heard what was being said.
Sense of smell	Malcolm does not like the smell of fish at all.
Sense of taste	Malcolm does not like the taste of fish or anything fishy.

Sense of touch 	Malcolm will jump if you touch him without any warning. He finds it difficult to predict when someone might touch him so it can be a real shock.
Sense of balance 	Malcolm is quite heavy on his feet and can lose his balance from time to time. This is especially true when he is anxious.
Sense of space 	Malcolm does not like people getting too close to him but will often invade other people's personal space, he does not seem to understand it.

Development – making good use of the person's strengths

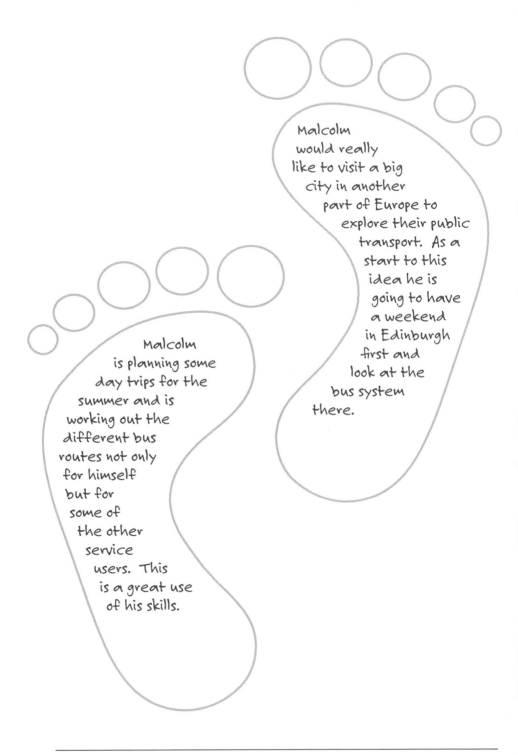

Malcolm would really like to visit a big city in another part of Europe to explore their public transport. As a start to this idea he is going to have a weekend in Edinburgh first and look at the bus system there.

Malcolm is planning some day trips for the summer and is working out the different bus routes not only for himself but for some of the other service users. This is a great use of his skills.

The support they need to reduce their struggles

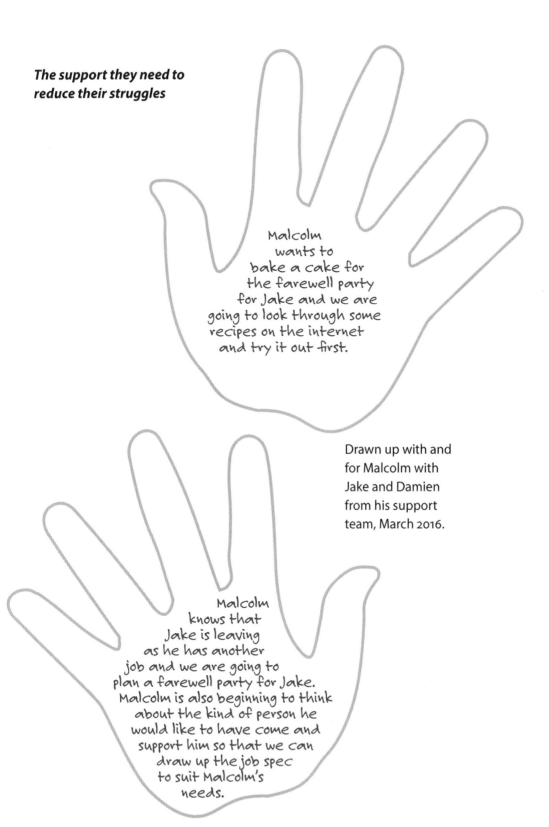

Malcolm
wants to
bake a cake for
the farewell party
for Jake and we are
going to look through some
recipes on the internet
and try it out first.

Drawn up with and
for Malcolm with
Jake and Damien
from his support
team, March 2016.

Malcolm
knows that
Jake is leaving
as he has another
job and we are going to
plan a farewell party for Jake.
Malcolm is also beginning to think
about the kind of person he
would like to have come and
support him so that we can
draw up the job spec
to suit Malcolm's
needs.

One of the things I have found of interest when working with staff teams is the lack of knowledge around sensory issues for people with autism which is something the basic autism profile can help with.

Consider Anna, who gets very anxious at the supermarket and begins to display behaviour that is a challenge for the staff. This can easily lead staff to believe that she does not like going to the supermarket, does not like shopping and it should be deleted from her activity schedule. Anna actually loves to go shopping, but she finds the hustle and bustle of a busy supermarket with lights and music rather overwhelming for her sensory processing capabilities. Her behaviour is a reaction to this experience of sensory overload and she responds in the most familiar and predictable pattern for her in order to try and reduce her own anxiety, but for the staff this is a real challenge.

Fortunately for Anna her keyworker is currently developing an autism profile about Anna and Anna's autism. With this in place and with a much better understanding of Anna's sensitivity to noise and lights they try the local corner shop for her to pick a magazine for herself, which she does and she wants to look round the shop. It is seen as a risk, but one worth taking and so this eventually becomes part of her activity schedule and Anna is always keen when it comes to 'corner shop time.'

Anna indicates positively this is something she is choosing to do. But it is quite a while before this is taken any further and someone suggests extending this activity and trying the supermarket trip again. This time, with a well-developed autism profile, the suggestion is made for Anna to visit the 24 hour supermarket when it is quiet in the late evening. A member of staff also contacts the store manager and requests that the music be turned off between 9 and 10pm on a Wednesday evening to see if this will help Anna cope with the experience and be able to enjoy it more. It works and Anna selects her magazine and enjoys wondering around the shop, hardly seeing another person, but every now and then selecting an item of food to put in her shopping basket. The trip lasts over an hour and Anna returns home very happy having made some clear choices about what she likes and wants, but in an environment that her sensory processing system can cope with.

Jayden was doing very well developing his independence skills in the family home with the support he received. He had learnt to prepare and cook a number of meals and was proud of his abilities. When the time came for him to move into supported living staff were confident he would do well. Jayden seemed to be reasonably happy in the flat and he had been very involved in choosing furniture and making his bedroom a lot like his bedroom at home. However once he had moved in he simply refused to cook. Jayden uses language to communicate and it was very hard for staff to understand why he didn't want to cook but he just made sandwiches all the time and said that was what he wanted to eat.

It took an autism intelligent member of the staff team to sort this situation out and it could have been so easy to say, *"Oh well, if that's what he wants to eat it's up to him, it's his choice."*

Cooking is a very sensory experience and for Jayden the amount of change that he had experienced was tough, but the kitchen was a bridge too far. The lighting was different, the feel of the pans and the crockery was different. Even the smell of the food waste bin for vegetable peelings was not something he had experienced before. At home he had a pot to put the peelings in and then his Mum transferred them to the food waste because she knew he did not like the smell. The food itself looked and tasted different – the local supermarket was a different brand to the one used by his Mum for shopping and so it went on until staff began to think in an autism intelligent way.

The suggestion was made that when he went for a visit to the family home one day he should offer to cook one of his delicious dishes for his family as they had missed his cooking. Jayden's member of support staff would come to watch and learn so that she could find out how to cook this meal for Jayden. This was successful and having had this experience staff were able to see and sense themselves what was different in the kitchen in Jayden's family home and how they could support him better, to enable him to cook at his own flat. With this experience, the staff set about making the kitchen more like his home. They got a pot for the peelings, some utensils that were the same and suggested for the next shop that they go to a supermarket that was the same brand as the one his Mum used. They also changed the bulbs in the kitchen so there were no longer bright spotlights, but a gentler light. The member of staff then offered to cook one of Jayden's signature dishes, but seeking his guidance. It did not take long before Jayden was not only correcting the member of staff about which way the saucepan handle should be on the stove, but he had taken over and prepared a delicious pasta dish.

Without the insight of that member of staff and the willingness to say, *"I will cook and you can remind me of what to do"* Jayden could still be living on sandwiches today because it was initially seen as his choice. Thankfully he isn't and he can now cook six different dishes and does so regularly, using the familiar pot for his peelings that staff empty into the food waste bin kept outside, using ingredients from a supermarket that is not the closest to where he lives, but is the same brand as the one his Mum uses and with saucepans that have the same kind of handles as those his Mum has at home. This is an autism friendly way of working thanks to an autism intelligent member of the staff team.

Remember:

- Sensory issues for people with autism are so much more than about noise sensitivity, it is about all the senses

- For some people with autism what we experience as an unpleasant smell can be completely overwhelming for them

- Don't expect the person with autism to necessarily be able to explain their sensory reaction to you, but do take it seriously

- Become a good autism detective, observe and learn. This can lead to a good profile of the way autism impacts for each person

- Keep the autism profile live and under review

- Become autism friendly and autism intelligent

5. The ability to shift attention

Many people on the autism spectrum who have published their autobiographical accounts speak about the difficulty in shifting attention. Donna Williams (Williams, 1998) refers to herself as being 'mono-channelled.' Wendy Lawson (Lawson, 2001) talks of not hearing the teacher telling her off at school as she was visually absorbed by the grain of the wood in her desk. She did not mean to appear rude, she was not 'choosing' to be disobedient, but she was unable to shift her attention from one thing to another easily. For most of us the shout from a teacher or parent or colleague would cause an instant shift in attention and our ability to then focus on what was being said. It is not the same for people with autism and it is another area that requires understanding and adapting to, especially in relation to choice and autism.

Another true story is about John eating his lunch. On this day it happens to be a favourite – meat pie, mash and peas. Slowly and with some sadness he

Choice and control the autism friendly way

is coming to the end of his meal. A member of staff calls over to him, *"Come on John, we are off to the velodrome to go cycling and you love cycling"*, the staff member also mimes cycling to support John's understanding. John says clearly and firmly *"No"*, turning back to those last few mouthfuls. The member of staff trying to be encouraging and supportive comes across to John and begins to try and persuade him to get a move on, knowing that cycling is an activity John enjoys, but with no awareness of John's difficulty in shifting his attention from the meal to what is being said.

It ends with John becoming angry and hitting a member of staff after first being left in peace to enjoy the last moments of meat pie, mash and peas. Once it had all been eaten John is ready to go to the velodrome but is told he chose not to go.

There was a great deal going on here for Joe, the sensory experience of the meal he loved, the words being spoken that he was not processing and not being able to shift his attention quickly in the way so many of us do in an instant.

There are many incidents of people with autism being thought to be deaf as they do not respond when called or not even to loud noises suddenly happening close by. Slowly the understanding of what it is like to be absorbed by one thing to the complete exclusion of all else is being acknowledged and taken account of.

Temple Grandin in the film *A is for autism* (Webb, 1992) speaks about how as a child she was totally absorbed by a spinning coin and how this blocked out all other sounds, even something being smashed behind her. This ability to focus on one thing can bring with it great gifts and skills as Temple Grandin has illustrated in her lifelong career researching the care and welfare of cattle (Grandin and Johnson, 2009). However, in terms of staff in services for people with learning disabilities who may be unlikely to understand the issues for people with autism around attention shifting, we need to develop an awareness so that supporting the concept of choice will not be such a struggle for people with autism or for the staff. In the case of John above, he was not choosing to stay behind and miss the cycling session, he was concentrating on the here and now – his favourite meal. He certainly did want to go cycling, but it appeared to the staff member that John was making a choice, even though she thought that was the wrong choice. To his great distress, John was left behind and missed out on an activity he really liked to take part in. No one had a good afternoon. The staff member was trying to do the right thing, remind John it was a favourite activity of his that was about to happen and if he did not hurry he might miss out. However, this did not take account of John being on the autism spectrum and what that meant for John as he was focused on his meat pie, mash and peas.

Time is a challenging concept and one that many people with autism have problems with. The importance of words like 'now' and 'next' can't be stressed enough as autism friendly language to help give a time frame to what is happening. Time is quite abstract and being able to read a clock face does not necessarily mean you can judge the passing of time or have a concept of how long it may take to do the hoovering before you can have a cup of tea. One of the most useful tools in your autism friendly toolbox are sand timers. With a sand timer you can actually see time passing. Many people with autism find them so helpful and calming. They make what is abstract concrete and visible. You can get them large and small for a wide range of times. In relation to John, if he is told that it's lunchtime now and that next he is going to the velodrome, then lunch needs to be given the time to be eaten. As staff, we need to plan and prepare well so we are not rushing or hurrying people. It is equally important to make sure we do stick to the things we say and not get people ready for an activity and then spend time hunting for the keys for the minibus. Find the keys first.

The good news for John and his now, well developed autism profile, is that he always has time to focus on his food and enjoy it. Starting lunch earlier has helped this. Once he has eaten lunch, he has what is coming next in the picture of him at the velodrome or whatever his afternoon activity is. John then calmly takes his plate out to the kitchen and collects the things he requires for his next activity. There are no temper outbursts and no one gets hit.

Remember:

- People with autism are often very focused and absorbed by one thing at a time.

- It is better if we can give a warning that things are going to change and they need to begin to give their focus and attention to something else.

- Visual supports that aid an understanding of time passing can be very useful. For example, sand timers, traffic light cards, a clock.

- Try to ensure people do have the time they need to eat a meal or take part in an activity.

6. Experience of stress and anxiety

> *"Anxiety as an indicator that someone with autism is experiencing stress was associated with autism as early as Kanner's (1943) first description of the syndrome."*

(Grace Baron et al, 2006)

It often feels to me that though we know stress and anxiety are closely associated with autism, we fail to recognise the behaviour that is a result of the stress experienced. Of course, this in turn has an effect on choices and how they are made but if we are going to support people in their choice making we need to once again have a better understanding of their autism.

One of the common issues raised with me by staff who work in supported living services with people with autism is the amount of time people can spend on their computers, gaming into the small hours and they then struggle to get up in the morning. Many staff think this is the person's choice. Gaming for hours is likely to be the main form of stress relief for the person and certainly their main 'special interest'. Understanding the significance of special interests needs to form part of an autism profile for a person, and how a person's special interest might be important for them in reducing their stress.

In the case of one particular young man, staff discovered that he found his morning routine of having a shower and a shave before breakfast quite stressful and he got anxious about having enough time to eat his breakfast before it was time to go to his college course. However, this was something he was not able to explain and it took an autism friendly member of staff to work out that anxiety over the mornings was the root cause of him needing to stay gaming until the early hours. The gaming was for him a real stress reliever and firmly a special interest that he loved to take part in and if possible spend hours doing. So after a day of being social (very tiring for people with autism) and to ward off the building anxiety about the next morning, this man settled down to gaming as early as he could and remained on it as long as he could.

It took an autism friendly member of staff to take the focus off the perceived problem, which was the amount of time spent gaming and to focus more on what it was about the morning routine that he found to be stressful. By reducing the morning stress they were able to support the young man to reduce the amount of time he spent gaming.

It was the shower that was a problem. Joel, the man concerned, did not enjoy the experience of a shower – he knew and accepted it needed to happen, but even thinking about it made him anxious. Coupled with the fact he had to shave, clean his teeth and have breakfast was all too much in the morning and he was only just about coping. His strategy for coping was to spend as much time as possible gaming at night which resulted in him being overtired in a morning and so the getting up routine was even more stressful.

Quite simply, the shower was scrapped and he had a bath before he went to bed, much more enjoyable as Joel agreed. It would not suit all of us, but I know a number of people with autism who prefer to shower or bath at night than in the morning as waking up and getting up on their own can be quite a stressful experience. The gaming was then reduced as there was a time set aside for Joel to have his bath.

Once again, so many issues are involved – Joel can talk well, but he was not able to explain his feelings about the situation. He wanted and needed predictability and the gaming really gave him this. The morning routine was predictable, but from a sensory angle it was stressful. For the staff it was becoming autism friendly, together with the creation of a good autism profile that helped gain a better understanding of Joel and for Joel to understand himself.

I sometimes speak in training about being an autism detective. This is something so much easier to do once the steps have been taken from just being aware of the autism to being able to work in a more autism friendly way. This happens once autism is better understood and the more you get to know how autism affects each of the people you support. Additional training and ongoing learning about autism all help to develop autism friendly ways of working. A good level of knowledge gives you the skills to do the detective work that is often required to figure out why someone with autism is behaving in a particular way and what the struggles they are having are really about. As you begin to develop real autism intelligence, you can begin to hone those much needed detective skills. This is precisely what happened with the member of staff working with Joel as she made good use of his autism profile and worked out there were a number of factors leading to his stress and anxiety but by working in an autism intelligent way, they could be understood and Joel's needs met.

The stress decreased and Joel was better able to listen and understand, better able to accept a change of plan and more able to make a positive choice and contribute to his wellbeing by having a bath at night.

I have mentioned above in the story about Joel the concept of the 'special interest' which is very well explained by Tony Attwood (Attwood, 2008). He explains how the special interest can often be a real comfort to people with autism and a way of making sense of a confusing world. For people who do not know what to do or say at break time in school, talking about your special interest in washing machines brings some relief to the anxiety experienced by the stressful situation of an unstructured break time with lots of other children you do not know how to interact with.

In relation to choice, we need to understand the role special interests can play in reducing stress and anxiety, but equally we need to take care not just to leave people to their special interest assuming this is the *choice* they have made. They may well be choosing it because they are anxious and talking about washing machines is familiar, predictable and calming.

John Simpson (Hatton and Simpson, 2012) talks of his special interest in football and how once he got to understand himself and his autism better, he became aware that choosing to watch every match there was on television was actually preventing him from taking part in other activities he thought he would enjoy if he was not so anxious about how to cope in social settings. However John, now very self-aware, also knows he needs to have a certain amount of football to maintain his wellbeing in an autism friendly way.

Stress and anxiety and strategies to reduce them play a key role in the lives of people on the autism spectrum and as staff seeking to support and work with them, we need to be on the lookout for the causes of stress, the things that make people anxious and ask how we can reduce them. Very often when faced with difficulties, if we can reduce the experience of stress, the difficulties that are being presented by the person reduce, as in the way described earlier for Joel.

Remember:

- Most people with autism experience a higher than average level of stress and anxiety in their lives.

- Special interests are often a way of absorbing the person and bring relief from the stress that life in a social world can bring.

- Once again as support staff we need to hone our detective skills and be good observers, seeking to identify the possible causes of a person's stress.

- When a challenge occurs when you are working with someone with autism, look for the stress factor. If this can be reduced, the challenge being presented will reduce, even if they are not obviously related to each other.

Understanding autism takes time and is very much a lifelong job. It does not happen with a day's training or the completion of an e-learning module. It is a different way of thinking and being. The more you begin to understand this complex neuro-developmental difference the more you also see that choice plays a large part in creating anxiety. We need to support people to cope with making choices and learning how to make choices by taking those steps from autism awareness to working in an autism friendly way and eventually to becoming autism intelligent practitioners. This includes our ability to be a good autism detective as we watch, observe and seek to really understand the very different way of thinking that people with autism have.

I have spoken quite a bit about being autism aware, autism friendly and autism intelligent. For me these steps can only be taken over a period of time and as experience with different people on the autism spectrum grows. The more knowledge you acquire about autism and the more varied experiences you have in working with a range of people who have the diagnosis, the more steps you will take along what I see as a pathway. We become autism aware and begin to realise that why people do things is not likely to be for the reason we originally thought. This is when the light first switches on. Next comes the ability to make use of that awareness in the ways you work and learning to say less and to make use of something visual are indicators that the autism awareness has grown into an ability to be autism friendly. To take the next step and constantly find yourself able to think in autism intelligent ways comes neither quickly or easily in my experience. It takes work and practice, but it is what we need to do.

Chapter 4

Making choices is more complex when you have autism

Alex is a young man with autism I have known for many years and worked with when he was a teenager. We have written this chapter together and it begins with Alex's voice:

Alex:

I have known Sue for about 15 years. She taught at the residential special school I attended from 13 to 19. When it came to the time for me to leave school at first I told my parents and my social worker I did not need any support and I would be fine living on my own. I knew as an adult I could make these decisions, it was my choice. I like things being MY choice.

Sue and I did a project together because Sue felt I did not really know what it might be like to live on my own with no support. Before I left school I had staff around me all the time including waking night staff. Our project meant we went to visit lots of different places that people who have autism live in, people like me. These are the people we visited:

A man called Jonathon – he had his own flat, he had a job in a kitchen and went to work every day. He had a support worker who helped him manage his budget and take care of his flat and helped him to join in activities in the community.

I thought Jonathon's place was ok. It was quite small. I liked that he had a job and worked in a kitchen. I like to bake and would also like to work in a kitchen one day and be paid like Jonathon. I do have a voluntary job in a kitchen.

I visited a residential home for several people with autism living together. I decided I did not want to live with lots of other people with autism like this.

I visited a place where people had their own little flats but there were also areas that they shared together and there were staff there all the time. I felt I did not need staff with me all the time.

I went to visit David who has autism and who hardly had any support at all. He just had a visit once a month from someone to check he was ok. His flat was very, very small. It was very dirty. He only had fish fingers in the freezer to eat. He did not have a good TV. He did not have a mobile phone. He said he could not afford these things. He did not work. There was only one chair to sit on. I did not like this very much and it made me think that I might need some support.

After each visit Sue and I wrote about the things I liked and the things I did not like about each place. We wrote about what it would be like for me to live in places like the ones I visited. We used this to help me make a final decision about where I would like to go to live and the kind of support I would like to have. I finally chose to live in a house by myself or with one other person (it has ended up being by myself which I am happy with) and I chose to have support. Making all these visits helped me to make a decision and it was a different decision after the visits than before we went on them.

Sue says:

This was time consuming and hard work. We had to set up the visits and take Alex to each of them plus the write up and the time to reflect on each of the visits carefully. This kind of reflection is quite hard for people with autism as they live very much in the present moment, so it was really important when we were in each situation to make notes and to get Alex's thoughts down on paper the same day of the visit. I was trying to give Alex the opportunity to physically sit in the different places to experience the choices he could make and to physically see the consequences of those choices, albeit in the lives of other people. Alex did not like what he experienced when he went to see David. He was very clear that he did not want to live like that. I explained that once you say you do not need help or support it can be hard to get it back again so Alex made the decision to have some support in the house he finally moved into. It was and still is a housing association property with him as the tenant and with support staff coming in.

Alex:

> I still live in the same house and I still have some support, I have 15 hours a week. There are things I like about my house but there are also things that I don't really like. I like being independent and like making my own choices but I have a lot of anxiety and stress and I worry about things a great deal. I know Sue thinks it would be good if I had more support but I only want support from the people I know who have supported me for a long time. I don't want to have anyone new unless I know them.
>
> I don't like the fact that my house is often dirty. I do clean my kitchen with some help from my support worker when I am going to do my baking but I don't clean the rest of the house much. I find it hard to know what to do.
>
> I have some problems with my personal hygiene but I find it difficult to be motivated to keep myself clean unless there is what I see as a very good reason. I will clean myself to do my baking. I will clean myself if I am going to see Sue because she won't want to have lunch with me if I am not clean. But I don't wash or shower otherwise. I don't clean my teeth, as I don't believe it matters if you have dirty teeth. I don't really care what other people think unless it is going to affect me like if Sue would not have lunch with me, that would not be good.

Sue says:

I have kept in touch with Alex over the years and in many ways he did well leaving a residential special school with lots of staff often working 1:1. In fact when Alex first came to the school he was on a 2:1 staff ratio and I can remember a deputation from staff requesting he be on a 3:1 ratio due to his extreme challenging behaviour. What a difference now! He lives on his own with 15 hours support a week, but this also means that often Alex is living in a very dirty house and he gets extremely anxious. In fact when I first spoke to Alex about this book and that I would really like to involve him this is what he wrote to me via email:

"I don't know what good choices I make as I make so many bad choices. The bad choices I make are choosing not to wash regularly enough, choosing not to brush my teeth, choosing not to change my bed sheets, choosing not to clean my house often enough. I do make some silly choices like not eating all day and giving myself a headache. It does not bother me sleeping in a dirty bed plus I need help to change my bed sheets."

Sue continues:

I do not think Alex is making informed choices. I don't think Alex is lazy as some might say, rather I think he really doesn't understand how to do quite basic things. I say this because recently I offered, along with a friend who also knows Alex, to go to his house and help him clean his bedroom and change his bed sheets. Alex wanted this help and agreed to it almost instantly. It took a little time to organise as I felt he would need a new mattress having slept directly on the mattress for so many months. Alex's mother informed me that there was some new bed linen that had never been opened. I told Alex that my friend Linda and I would come and we would help him to clean his bedroom. I said I would buy a new duvet, two bottom sheets and some new pillows and pillow cases. We would use the new duvet covers he had that his mother had told us about. I also said Alex needed to buy a new mattress.

Alex bought the mattress. Linda and I turned up with cleaning materials and black sacks and we began. Alex did not sit down and leave us to it. He did however wait until he was told what to do. On the floor in the bedroom and on the landing were piles of clothes. Some were dirty and some were clean. It soon became clear that Alex did not know how to put clothes away. I showed him how to fold a jumper, we cleared a space on a chest of drawers and I asked Alex to collect all his jumpers and fold them on top of the drawers, he did this. Then Alex helped to sort the rubbish in the room (this included old food, broken glass, cables, old lamps, other electrical goods that no longer worked). Alex then did the hard physical work of taking the sacks of rubbish down stairs and making a pile outside the front door. Alex only stood still when he did not know what to do. When it was explained to him how to sort dirty clothes from clean clothes, he did it. I felt then and continue to feel that often Alex says he is making a choice when the truth is he does not understand how to do most of the things people suggest so he says he chooses not to do them. For Alex, leaving everything all over the floor makes for predictability and as we have covered in the previous chapter predictability is the one thing that helps people with autism remain calm. It does not need to be a predictability that is liked or wanted but it does need to be predictable.

Linda, Alex and I worked hard for three hours. We cleared, cleaned, hoovered and dusted. Linda's husband came with a large car and took the old mattress and some broken furniture and about ten sacks of rubbish to the tip. The following day Alex slept in clean sheets in a tidy room and he sent me this text:

> *"I felt good when I went to bed last night, my bedroom feels much more relaxing."*

Without direction and support to do basic mundane tasks Alex cannot do them so he appears to choose not to do them. He is of course saying he does not want to do them, but if supported, guided and directed I believe Alex does prefer to sleep in a clean bed, he just does not really know how to go about making it happen – choosing not to is easier and more predictable. Alex's verbal ability as someone with autism with a very uneven profile of development makes him appear more able than he is in many ways and so when he says, *"I don't care my bed is dirty, I choose to sleep in it like that"*, this is taken at face value with the belief that Alex is truly making a choice. I do not believe this is the case, but it is hard to get others to see that when Alex speaks so well and says some of the things he does. This is where support staff need to take the steps from being autism aware to being autism friendly and then continuing on to working in an autism intelligent way. I do not believe Alex really chooses to sleep in dirty sheets, he does prefer a clean bedroom but he does not know how to do this on his own and needs a considerable amount of support. The level of support needed does not seem to make sense with someone so verbally able, but it is genuinely required.

In an email Alex wrote to me he said:

> *"I realise there are choices to make but at the moment I am not doing anything, I wake up at 7.20am and I think about my anxieties. I then make a cup of coffee. I then go and get dressed. I then sit downstairs in my lounge sometimes for hours. At this time I could think about my choices, I could set aside an hour a day to do some cleaning but I don't."*

Alex sat in his living room

My argument is that if Alex was supported to clean his bedroom regularly, shown how to do this and a plan created, in time he could do more for himself but it will not come easily and I would anticipate him needing support to do this for a long time. The more times the bedroom was cleaned the more this would become the predictable pattern. The more predictable the pattern the more, I believe, Alex will want the pattern and be able to follow it. This will become a positive predictable pattern. In staff training, I often talk about the need for us to support the development of positive predictable patterns. Predictable patterns are what people with autism want and need. They will always happen and if we as support staff are not involved in helping them to be positive ones then they will very quickly become negative patterns. Sadly, negative predictability is easier to achieve and to get a positive predictable pattern we sometimes have to appear to go against what looks like a person with autism making a choice when they are not really. They are falling into a negative but predictable pattern because they do not really know how to do things differently. But given support and clear guidance, Alex can and does say that he prefers clean bed sheets. Getting them seems so complex he reverts to saying he chooses to have dirty ones.

The need for predictability is what often drives the choices made for so many people with autism, those who can speak and those who can't. John Simpson (Hatton and Simpson, 2012) says for him *"Autism is the quest for predictability."* In those vacuums of time when it is not clear what is happening, very often someone with autism will make something happen in order to ensure a pattern gets going and they can feel calmer. It may be that they begin to self-harm so staff will encourage them not to. They may start to strip off so that staff support them to keep their clothes on. They may begin to smear faeces so that staff will get them to help clean it up and clean themselves. All of these things create patterns, negative predictable patterns, but they are not really choices because making choices is more complex in autism. We need to grasp this in order to understand how to support someone who is choosing to stay in their room all day to be able to choose to join in an activity and benefit from the choice they did not think they could make. This is when we begin to work in an autism intelligent way but it does not come easily for us as staff. We need a good level of knowledge and understanding of autism and we need to be creative and imaginative about how we approach the many negative predictable patterns that can build up in people's lives. This is very true for Alex and continues to be so at the moment. He knows I hope it will change and at some point I am sure Linda and I will offer to go and help him clean his bedroom again because he struggles so much to be self-motivated and to understand the steps to changing his bed and being able to do it.

Tom Boughton (Hatton and Boughton, 2011) and I have a code word for the need for predictability when making a choice and how that can sometimes be not what a person really wants. Tom refers to it as 'frozen chickens'. This is because many years ago when he was due to leave college, Tom wanted some kind of predictable thing to happen and he was desperate to find something – anything. At the time I felt there was a real danger of him making a choice just to have some kind of predictability in his life. I spent time with Tom and painted the picture to him of being able to work 24 hours a day in a frozen chicken factory. His first response was, *"Yes please, can I?"* However, when I explained to him that this would mean not being able to listen to his favourite radio programme, The Archers, no time for his favourite food or drink, no time for his beloved visits to the library, slowly Tom began to see that working in a frozen chicken factory 24 hours a day might not be a choice that he really wanted to make. This realisation did not come easily. We will go on to look at how we can enable and facilitate choice for people with autism, but I believe there is a real need to first of all understand that it is not just a matter of saying, *"Well he's an adult and if that is what he chooses to do, it's up to him."* As staff working with people with autism there is so much more we should do.

Alex rang me very recently and said:

> "I have been thinking about what you said Sue, about needing more support to help me with my anxieties and to support me to do things. I am going to think about doing this. I am."

Alex has been thinking about this for many years and as I no longer work directly with him, or for the company that support him, I can only encourage and suggest from the side lines, something that I will continue to do. I do know it is not easy supporting Alex and he can be very frustrating but I do believe if staff were able to take those additional steps they would see that by being autism intelligent they would be able to support Alex into more positive predictable patterns and Alex would have a cleaner house and be pleased with this. As with the choices he made when first leaving school, this will take time and effort.

Remember:

- People with autism will choose what is most familiar and most predictable unless they are supported to really see what a different choice would be like.

- It is not really about support staff being good at persuasion but about us as support staff taking the time to support the person to have and see different experiences in order to make an informed choice.

- If someone with autism has good verbal skills, this does not mean they know how to do the many things we take for granted, for example how to boil an egg, cross the road and how to change bed sheets.

- Always be prepared to be surprised by the people with autism you support. They will surprise you with what they can do and how clever they are in certain ways and they will also surprise you by what they can't do and what they really struggle with.

Chapter 5

Risky choices

Tracey is someone with autism I have got to know more recently. She is 20 years old having received her diagnosis when she was 18. Up until the age of 18 Tracey struggled with her day to day life. She did not really make sense to herself or to her family and those around her. Tracey did not understand how relationships and friendships worked, but she tried to have them and she got into a number of difficulties. She felt confused and frustrated a lot of the time and would have outbursts of temper that resembled a toddler tantrum. These uncontrollable outbursts eventually led to her mum seeking help and finally to a diagnosis of autism. Tracey moved from the family home into supported living with three other young women where staff are employed to support them all on a 24 hour basis. It was in this setting that Tracey and I first met because, even though she now had a diagnosis of autism, she continued to have outbursts of anger and staff found it a considerable challenge to work with and support her. Tracey liked to use the internet and meet people online as she felt this was a great way to get friends.

When I first met Tracey, I thought here was someone with autism who is very verbal and like Alex her verbal ability completely masked her inability to understand herself and how the world worked. Like all people with autism, Tracey has a very uneven developmental profile. There are things she can do and that she is very good at, but she also has huge areas of difficulty. Staff were amazed by the things Tracey did not seem to understand, for example she didn't understand that if you leave a pan with an omelette in on the stove it will burn quickly and easily. In order to get a clearer picture of who Tracey is, as a person with autism, she and I began to work on a profile of her autism and this began to help Tracey understand for the first time what the diagnosis she had received two years previously actually meant. This is a way of working I encourage staff teams to take by working together and completing an autism profile to include the viewpoints of the person themselves if they are able to, each staff member, plus a parent or other family member. It is a very valuable way of learning to *Think Autism* the title of the updated Autism Strategy for England (Department of Health, 2014) and referred to in an article I wrote for the Good Autism Practice journal (Hatton, 2015).

So what did we learn from this amalgamated profile of how autism impacted upon Tracey? Staff were concerned about a number of choices that Tracey was making. They were also very aware that from their understanding of the Mental Capacity Act 2005 (MCA), Tracey was considered by them to have capacity in terms of making relationships and could therefore make these choices even if the staff team felt them to be unwise. It would be beneficial for staff supporting those who are vulnerable to have a good understanding of the MCA as it is an important piece of legislation. It carefully seeks to protect people like Tracey who has autism as well as those with dementia, brain injury, mental health conditions, etc. from decisions being made about them without their consent or without them being given the opportunity to try and understand. It also enshrines the need for family, support staff and other professionals to empower people to make decisions where they are able to. For example, it may be considered that a person does not have the capacity to make a large financial decision about paying for their care but they may well be able to decide what to buy for their shopping each week and how much to spend. Capacity has to be looked at on different levels and in all areas, it is not just a matter of saying someone does not have capacity and taking all their decisions for them. Nor is it simply a matter of saying they have capacity and so there is nothing that can be done to question that in relation to specific issues and circumstances. The MCA also stipulates that people can make decisions that may seem unwise to others as this does not mean they necessarily lack capacity. The staff working with Tracey were aware of this.

It does get quite complex at this point as the MCA talks about supporting someone to make a decision by giving them information that they can then weigh up. With information about the consequences of different decisions, they can make an informed choice. I think after reading Alex's story you will see that 'informed choice' for people with autism is not just a matter of telling them about the consequences. Time needs to be taken to work in autism intelligent ways to help them see the consequences and especially for them to understand, where possible, that the most predictable outcome might not be the one they really want.

When I started working with Tracey she was making choices and some of them were quite risky, particularly in terms of meeting strangers she had met over the internet and also in her attitude to taking pills. It was around the consequences of the choices being made that Tracey needed so much help with and this was not obvious when meeting her. It was also something that Tracey struggled to understand as she lives very much in the moment and struggles to see what could happen because of a choice she has made. Giving her a better understanding of her own autism really began to help her become more aware of this difficulty. I wanted to do this work hoping that if she understood herself better and the particular difficulties she has in understanding how relationships work and what goes on in other people's minds, she would more readily seek support and guidance from those she knows and trusts.

Tracey was making decisions in two quite specific areas of difficulty for people with autism. The first was concerned with meeting people over the internet which of course many people do, but Tracey has autism and this means she has difficulty understanding how other people's minds work. Tracey was completely unaware that people could be different from the way they described themselves online. She did not understand that someone could say they were a 21-year-old man with dark hair and brown eyes who loves to build with Lego like Tracey does and yet in reality be aged 54 and bald. Tracey's level of naivety online was that of a young child. Not only did Tracey not really understand, the staff working with her did not quite grasp how vulnerable she was. Tracey talks well, she is good with a computer and her lack of understanding about how relationships work is hidden, especially when making relationships over the internet.

Tracey was using the internet to make friends, join chatrooms and agreeing to meet people, and as an adult you might ask, why shouldn't she? In fact, as a result, Tracey has got herself into some dangerous situations risking both physical and sexual abuse. It may be surprising or even shocking to people reading this book that as Tracey gained more insight into herself and her own autism, she was supported and encouraged to stop using the internet completely. People on the autism spectrum are very black and white and it can take time to see the possibilities of doing anything in-between. For Tracey, as she became aware for the first time that it is possible for people to say one thing about themselves and the truth to be completely different, stopping all use of the internet seemed the only way forward.

Tracey says:

> I keep off the internet at the moment, I have got myself into danger going on dating sites and into chatrooms. People want to meet me and I don't know anything about them, so with staff help I am keeping away from the internet, it may be different in the future but at the moment this feels best for me.

Sue says:

This may be a very childlike decision to have supported and guided Tracey to make – all or nothing, when really, surely she could just learn to use the internet safely like most other adults? But Tracey is not like most other adults, she is someone who appears to have capabilities that she does not actually have. Tracey's level of social and emotional intelligence is years behind her ability to speak. Her ability to understand how relationships work and what to expect in friendships of different kinds is very limited and this became apparent when working with her on her autism profile. For the first time, I think Tracey began to see that she needed a lot of support to be able to make friends and certainly if she was to find a boy or girlfriend that could develop into a sexual relationship. Being encouraged to take this quite drastic step of stopping all access to the internet was, I believe, a good thing, even though it was taking choice away completely for a limited period.

Over a lengthy period of time with careful, thoughtful support, Tracey will learn more about the internet and how it works. This is where staff have to work in autism intelligent ways taking the time needed to support Tracey to a better understanding. Tracey is beginning to learn more about relationships and how they work. In time, and with some clear guidelines to stick to, she will be supported to access the internet again. The internet is a resource that for so many of us is just part of everyday life, we may make dozens of choices online every day if not every hour. But then our neurotypical brains work differently and we mostly weigh up choices and consider consequences with speed and with ease. Tracey cannot do this without considerable help, she is beginning to understand this about herself as she gets to know the nature of her own autism. It is a journey her staff team and indeed her mum are also travelling on together.

Another difficult part of her life Tracey wanted to share was to do with buying and having access to paracetamol.

Tracey says:

> I used to get angry and upset a lot, I still do sometimes. When I feel like this I need people to know and I need people to listen to me. If I say I have taken paracetamol, people always listen and things happen in a predictable pattern. I like this. I get taken to hospital and the doctors and nurses ask me questions and I like all this.

Sometimes I would say I had taken them even if I had not as the same pattern can happen and I get to go to hospital. This pattern helps me to calm down, then I feel better.

Staff have been helping me to understand the impact of me doing this on other people. They have helped me to understand that if the doctors and nurses are with me there may be people who are really ill who don't get a doctor or a nurse as they are busy with me. This could be dangerous for those people. I am learning to understand myself better and my autism. I am learning to get predictable patterns in different ways, in more positive ways. For example, telling the chemist not to sell me any paracetamol and for me to talk to staff before I start screaming and shouting or taking pills.

It is just that if you say you have taken pills things happen and I like it when things happen and I know I can control them in this way.

I also used to trash my bedroom regularly and it's kind of the same, things happen when you start to trash your bedroom. Staff come running and try to get me to stop. The more I have learnt about my autism the more I can see that I am searching for predictability when I feel anxious, and I get anxious when I am confused and don't know what's happening. This happens quite a lot. Perhaps a lot more than people would realise. People often see me as very capable because I talk well, but I need help to understand myself more and I need help to know what is happening. I need help to be able to see how my behaviour affects other people, as I don't see that very easily.

Learning about who it's safe to talk to has also been good. There are other people with autism who use what is called 'the hand of trust'. I have got a poster with a hand on it and against each finger and the thumb I have named someone in my life who I can trust, who I can talk to, who will listen to me and who will help guide me when I am making choices, when I am making decisions. I have found this really helpful.

Tracey's hand of trust

Sue says:

I have used the idea of a 'hand of trust' with many adults with autism once they begin to be aware of the difficulties they will always have in understanding how relationships work. They need help, support and guidance in areas of choice and decision making that as neurotypical adults we would not normally talk to other people about. I think it's important that the hand includes people who may have different opinions rather than just parents who may be quite restrictive due to the natural protective instincts we have towards our own children. If a hand of trust includes a range of different people who care, the person with autism can be supported to listen to the views and opinions given and come to a decision and be supported to act on it. This all takes time and is much more than just being autism aware or even autism friendly. To work in autism intelligent ways involves us being good autism detectives and working out the best way to support someone to make choices and decisions based on a real understanding of both consequences and impact on other people. It is of course also incredibly rewarding to work with someone like Tracey and see her come to a level of understanding about herself. This is an understanding that grows and develops with the questions she asks and when looking at her own profile. Each time we review the profile we see how Tracey has grown and come to understand herself and what the diagnosis means for her just that little bit more.

Back to Tracey:

> I want to give you some other examples of choices that are difficult for me. I like Pepsi and there is a pub near me that when you go for a meal you can have 'unlimited' Pepsi. That means you can keep going back and refilling your glass over and over and over again. I love Pepsi so without some help and guidance I will (in fact I have in the past) keep refilling my glass until I feel sick. I find it so very difficult to not do this. I like the predictability of filling my glass over and over again, but it doesn't make me feel very well. I need some support to make the better choice of limiting the amount of Pepsi I have and I find this really difficult to do on my own.

> A little while ago I was in another pub with Sue and she said something that was not very autism friendly. She was taking me out for a meal and she said, "Choose whatever you want Tracey, I am paying tonight so have what you like." She's supposed to know about autism and how difficult choice is for people with autism like me. I found this really hard, it made me feel anxious as there were so many things to choose and I did not know how to make a choice. I got more and more anxious, then Sue realised she had said something that was not very helpful for me. She apologised and I suggested a good way of helping me was to give me a price limit so that at least half of the menu was not available. This worked as now the choice was more limited and I felt less anxious. We had a nice meal together.

Sue says:

I may have been working with people with autism for a long time and may be well qualified but thinking in an autism friendly and autism intelligent way just does not come naturally as it is not how my brain works. I need, like all people working with people with autism, to make the conscious effort to think and check I am being autism friendly before I say and do things. On this occasion, like many others, I just forgot what caused Tracey to experience real anxiety. I believe this is something we do very regularly when working with people with autism and especially where choices are concerned. We have to become more aware of this and challenge the emphasis on choice in services for people with learning disabilities where people may also have autism. Their autism needs to be taken account of and this may mean limiting or restricting choice and at times taking choice away altogether and telling someone what to do. I think the experiences described in this chapter by Tracey help us to see that even someone as able as Tracey really needs careful support and guidance in many areas of choice making. This form of support may not be suitable when working with someone with a learning disability who does not have autism.

What about choice for someone who is non-verbal? Should we just scrap the idea of choice and go back to making all their choices for them, as happened when I first came into this area of work 40 years ago? You might think this is where I am heading, but it is not. I do think there are times when, in order to reduce anxiety and to de-stress someone, we should take the choices away and just guide them to what we think is best, where this is an activity or a meal etc. But when they are calm and in a good place emotionally, that is the time to perhaps offer two choices. Over time and by becoming that good autism detective, we will get to know a person and when they can cope with choice and when not. With good observation, we can also learn when it might be a good idea to motivate someone to try something new. The new and different is almost always scary for a person with autism and will often be refused but with encouragement and a person centred motivator a new experience could later become a clear choice. To be a good autism detective, you need to be patient and observant, willing to take the time to really get to know someone. You also need to know and understand autism well so that you can put these two things together. Then you will have taken those steps from being autism aware, to working in autism friendly ways to really being able to work in an autism intelligent way. Though, as you can see from the mistakes I still make, we have to keep learning and keep working at this. It does not come naturally to those of us with more neurotypical brains, no matter how much experience we may have.

Take Samantha, who has a very restricted diet. Some of the staff supporting her said this was her choice. It is food that brings her predictability and this helps her to remain calm in a world she finds very confusing. When I worked with Samantha, my suggestion was that we try to introduce new food without any kind of force and in tiny amounts. The first of these was a single pea and using the autism friendly language of first the pea and then the fish fingers (her preferred food), she soon started to eat the pea. Slowly and steadily we built from this base, quite literally one pea at a time. Within a two year period, her diet that previously was based around three foods had grown to eleven different foods and she was making simple choices at meal times.

I believe at times it is right to take choice away and to restrict it. The reason for this is to de-stress the person and enable them to have a sense of calm. I do this because so many people with autism who can tell me say that choice is stressful.

I am very aware of the danger of people agreeing with me and becoming controlling in how they work, but still not really understanding autism and how it impacts on different people. This is why I refer to the steps support staff need to take when working with people who have autism, whether they have an additional learning disability or not. The first step of autism awareness is important but don't stop there. Learn how to work in autism friendly ways and keep learning to ensure you are able to take that third step and work in an autism intelligent way.

Tracey says:

I wanted to tell people about Dexter.

This is Dexter sitting with me. He is my toy dog and I used to need to take him everywhere with me which I know some people thought was silly as I am an adult. But Dexter is very important to me and I like to cuddle him. Thankfully staff have understood this and they did not try to stop me taking him with me. But they have helped me to see what other people might think about me. They have helped me to know that Dexter will be safe at home when I go out and I could just take something like a small toy from my room with me. I always look forward to seeing him again when I get back home.

Tracey with Dexter

Sue says:

For me this is a really good example of staff working with the choices Tracey was making and not denying her. Staff had become increasingly aware that in many ways Tracey is quite young emotionally and socially and this big cuddly dog really helps her. On this occasion the best thing was to accept the choice she was making, even though it made her appear odd to others when she was out in the community. Over time staff have supported Tracey to be able to leave Dexter at home, though he remains a significant part of her life and probably will do for a long while yet.

It is not simply that as staff 'we know best' because we don't. We have to understand autism, get to know the way autism is impacting on every person we work with and then begin to figure out how to work in a person centred way with each person. This is what I mean by working in an autism intelligent way. It takes learning and understanding. It also requires us to continually seek to see the world through the autism lens, fully aware that if our brain is neurotypical this will not come either naturally or easily.

Remember:

- Risky choices can and will be taken by people with autism and if we are supporting them we need to work extra hard to help them see the consequences and not just tell them about them.

- People with autism have an uneven developmental profile and may appear to be much more able than they are, in particular socially and emotionally. It is not that they can't develop in these areas but they need help and support that is ongoing.

- Where possible, working with the person on their autism profile and reviewing it with them is a good way of supporting them to understand their own autism and of seeing the progress made as staff work in more autism intelligent ways.

- Developing the autism profile will also enhance your autism detective skills through good observation and patience.

Choice and control the autism friendly way

Chapter 6

A parent's view on choice

It has been good to have the voices of two people on the autism spectrum in this book. I also wanted to ensure a parent gave their view on the topic of choice and my friend Linda Woodcock kindly agreed to contribute. She shares something of her own experience in relation to Christopher, her son and his choice. She then goes on to outline experiences from other people she knows in relation to choice.

Linda says:

> When I was asked to write this chapter I had already become aware just what a responsibility I had, given that I was a deputy for and administrator of, a personal budget for my 28-year-old son. Christopher had been diagnosed with autism and severe learning disability when he was three years old and we had come on a long and at times arduous journey, with many exclusions from schools, failed services and times when living with the challenges had pushed our family to the edge.

> I have always been conscious that although we had always tried to encourage Christopher to make positive choices in his daily life, he had little choice and control over what most of us take for granted – where he lived, who he lived with and who supported him on a daily basis. Therefore the responsibility for making the right choices for him lay firmly at my door – this was and still is the challenge and I do not nor should I do this alone.

> In 2010 we took Christopher out of his service which despite our best efforts could no longer meet his needs. We realised that having to share his space with others was impacting on him in a very negative way, his physical and mental health was deteriorating and we felt we had no choice. We made a pretty

momentous decision to bring him home which meant his father giving up his job to become his full time carer as our short term goal was to bring him back to health. This took 12 months and the next year was spent negotiating with social services to secure an individual budget which happened at the same time that we managed to find a brand new bungalow to rent in the village where we lived and Christopher had been brought up.

Our next job was to recruit a team to support Christopher and we were very lucky as some of the staff who had worked with him in his previous placement came to us and asked to work with him. We were all set. We were determined that as a team, giving Christopher a good day would be our main priority.

For the last six months of Christopher's placement in a service, he had an increasing amount of incidents where he was hitting out at other service users as well as staff and his self-injury was becoming more damaging. In the two years he spent at home, we had no incidents of physical outburst towards others and his self-injury had dramatically reduced. We wanted to maintain this and so we concentrated on providing a low arousal environment and making sure that those that supported him were as like-minded as his family. Christopher has a small and very stable team that has been in place for the last three years and for the main part, Christopher's wellbeing has certainly improved. However, we still must be mindful of the need to help Christopher make meaningful choices, whilst acknowledging that we, as his supporters, in fact make the big choices and therefore extra care has to be taken that we always have his best interests at the centre of any decisions we make.

What do we do when Christopher is so overwhelmed by sensory challenges that he is unable to leave his room for more than a few minutes at a time? Do we say well he didn't go out and that was his choice? Or do we say today Christopher cannot access community activities, but as a team we will monitor this and if this happens for more than two or three days we will come together to look at what we can do to help him through this. The use of visual support is very important, although it has been difficult for Christopher to be proactive in deciding his daily schedule,

*we have made sure his day reflects what we know he needs. It was,
however, a day of real joy when Christopher took off the picture
for lunch time picnic and rooted through his box and pulled out
a picture of McDonalds! He had made a meaningful choice.*

*For many families, having their adult child living in either
residential services or supported living presents them with many
dilemmas and frustrations. The mantra of 'they are an adult
now and can make their own choices' seems to mask what is
often not just a lack of understanding of autism but a lack of
acknowledgement of the overwhelming effects of sensory issues
for people with autism and the importance of informed choice.
In some cases, a negative attitude toward families exists right
across an organisation. Speaking at a recent international
conference, I asked the question, how many staff had received
training in working effectively with families? Only five people
raised their hands and yet when asked how many staff had
had difficult encounters with families, everyone raised their
hand. This is not just about our story.*

Sue says:

I do not believe the staff who were supporting Christopher when things went
so badly wrong for him were bad people. I am sure they knew Christopher
had autism and probably had some training, but it was by no means enough.
It takes time and a good level of knowledge of the individual to feel comfortable
enough to leave him in his bedroom for a day with a towel over his head. Staff
need to be willing to do the detective work to figure out what to do next and
what might be the autism intelligent way to support Christopher to a better
and calmer place where he is able to engage in his community. Linda and her
husband came to the conclusion that this was not possible unless they led the
way, selected the staff, ensured a high level of autism training and ensured that
Christopher's needs were met so he could blossom and develop. Three years on,
Christopher is physically well and engaging in activities in his community on
most days. Linda and her husband feel this is proof that they did the best thing
possible by bringing him home and then setting up this truly person centred
service for their son.

Linda goes on to share two other family stories as she is very aware that her way is not the only way.

Mary's story:

We always had a good relationship with staff at John's school so it came as quite a shock when he went into an adult service and we found ourselves being excluded from the decision making process altogether. When we took him back from home visits, we were often met by someone we had never seen before and we noticed he was gaining weight. We asked about increasing his exercise and to look at what he was eating every day. This was met with resistance and a reluctance to divulge any information and we were told by the staff they had to follow what John wanted and that they could not restrict his diet, which wasn't what we wanted at all. Eventually, we found out that because John vocalised a lot staff were going to a McDonalds drive through as they could order food without having to take him inside the restaurant and he was eating convenience foods pretty much on a daily basis. This was not about John making good choices, but rather the staff making bad choices.

Sue says:

There are several questions to be asked here – how much does John really understand about the choices he is apparently making? What support and guidance are staff being given in working with John in more autism friendly ways? Then of course, the issue over how to work effectively with families? I am regularly told that parents are over protective, won't let go and are difficult to work with. Knowing Linda very well and a number of other parents, it is not surprising they are difficult to work with. I know I would be if it was my son I was leaving in someone else's care. In order to provide good autism friendly support, staff need to find ways of working effectively with families. Something I learnt long ago, and especially from Linda, was the importance of listening to parents and other family members. How many of us know the 'back story' to the adult we may be supporting whose mum we find a bit of a nuisance? It was one of the first things Linda taught me, ask questions and listen to the journey each parent has taken with their child. It will be different for the dad as well as the mum, so you may have a lot of listening to do. However, in my experience, once you have made that investment of time, you are very likely to view the requests and comments from the parents quite differently. The best way is for staff and family members to be one team around the person seeking to work with them in a person centred and autism intelligent way. This does not happen easily, but when it does, you will see the individual develop and flourish in ways you may not have imagined possible.

Carol and Dave's story:

Peter was diagnosed with Asperger syndrome when he started senior school. It was clear that in many ways he was very clever and excelling in maths and IT. However, he struggled in other subjects such as English. As he entered his teenage years, he became obsessed with slot machines and started spending more money than he actually had and we were constantly under pressure to supply him with £1 coins. He started stealing them from my purse and no matter what sanctions we put in place, it made no difference. We hoped it would be a passing phase, but it continued. When, as an adult, he moved into supported living the problem got considerably worse. He began taking money from support staff and 'borrowing' money from others in his block. We became increasingly concerned and were told it was his choice to spend his money in this way and that we should let him take the consequences so he would learn from them. He was finally reported to the police and convicted of theft and his probation officer just kept trying to get him to go to Gamblers Anonymous. I tried to explain that it wasn't a compulsion to gamble, but rather he was fascinated by the sequence of the fruits as they landed on the screen.

We tried to get someone who understood his autism to work with him as it was clear that those supporting him had no experience of autism. However, we were excluded at every turn and yet it was us he turned to for money when he couldn't get it any other way. If we are talking about choice then ours was clear, either we let him take the consequences or else keep bailing him out. We continue to struggle with this and I expect always will.

Sue says:

Peter is an able young man in many ways and his abilities are masking the difficulties he has to the extent that support staff who may be 'aware' of his diagnosis have not been equipped to support him appropriately. Family and staff are not working together and the difficulties persist. This is a story not unfamiliar to me and one that cries out for some self-awareness work to be done with and for Peter. In addition, there is a need to help his support staff take some steps towards more autism friendly ways of working and ultimately into autism intelligent ways of supporting Peter to truly flourish as a human being.

Jackie's story:

Michael has autism and severe learning disabilities. I knew he needed to live on his own with support as most of the issues I'd had with services were about his hurting people who he lived with. I felt strongly that this was Michael telling us he found it impossible to tolerate other people around and in his space. However, the decision was made that he had to live in a shared house and it ended up with him being with other young men who were very similar to Michael. It did not surprise me at all that Michael soon began to make his feelings known in the only way he knew how to and that was to be violent and aggressive towards other people. The next step was to consider medication in order to help him calm down and reduce his anxiety. I felt if he could live in a quiet place with minimal disturbance, he would be calm. I eventually lost a long and hard battle against him being prescribed medication. They talked about best interests but the reality was the service was insisting that they would have to terminate his contract if we did not go down this route. Where was his choice in that? I kept saying he needed a different service and that he should live alone but the local authority was insistent that they were meeting his needs appropriately. It was all about cost and not about person centred ways of working and enabling people to have choice and control. For me it made discussions about whether he chose to go swimming or horse riding a bit of a nonsense. Michael did not want to live with other people.

We should all strive to offer as much choice as possible but it is not that clear cut when looking at the needs of people with autism. Those that care for and support them have a responsibility to make sure that offering choice is done in such a way as to make sure that the outcomes are positive. We need to acknowledge the complexity of the Mental Capacity Act when applying it to people like our son. There are some decisions he can make and some he needs a great deal of help with and some he is not able to make. As his family, we know him well and want and need to be involved in his ongoing care and support but we do not feel listened to or heard.

Back to Linda:

We need to acknowledge that generally the only constant in the lives of many vulnerable adults with autism is family and therefore it is imperative that family are included in the decision making process.

Too often, the idea of offering someone choice is in the context of financial constraints where there is clearly a conflict between cost and providing individualised services. If we cannot guarantee that those we love live in appropriate settings, supported by people who understand them and are willing to advocate for them, how can offering choices around daily life have the impact we want?

As parents, our overriding fear is what will happen to our loved ones when we are no longer here to care or advocate for them. We need to know that those we pass the mantle on to will, where appropriate, help our loved ones make informed choices and where this is not possible, make choices on their behalf which are not only in their best interests but have the best possible outcomes for their health and wellbeing.

Sue says:

Linda presents those of us who work in services with a real challenge, a challenge to listen to families and truly take account of what they are saying and to work in partnership with them when supporting people with autism. This in turn will help us to listen better to the individuals themselves. We know that all behaviour happens for a reason and is communicating something to us but do we really ask ourselves what the person is trying to say and are they making a choice that we are not hearing or even listening to? Families can give us valuable insights if we take the time to listen to their story and try to do something that is very hard for people with autism, but something we need to do in order to work in autism intelligent ways, that is to see things from other people's point of view and step inside their shoes.

Remember:

- Listen to the parents and other members of the family.
- Find out about the experiences of the family.
- Involve and seek guidance from family members who have known the person all their lives.
- Ensure staff receive training on working effectively with families.

Choice and control the autism friendly way

Chapter 7

Supporting choice making as a good autism practitioner

It will be clear by now that I consider issues around choice to be a real difficulty for people with autism. In part, there is a historical context as to why choice has become so important in services to warrant a book being written about the issue. However, the need also stems from my experience in a long career of working with people who have autism. I have maintained a relationship with many of them and seen grow from adolescents into mature men and women. All of them struggle with choice and decision making and I want to try to improve my own ability to help with this, as well as that of anyone supporting someone with autism and, of course, to help the people themselves.

Throughout this book I have talked about three key steps that I believe staff need to take if they are to become truly good autism practitioners. I want to expand on each of those steps to help staff work in an autism intelligent way. I will then give some examples of how to effectively support choice making and how to encourage and motivate people with autism to want to make interesting and innovative choices. However, this can only happen when people are calm and at ease with themselves. So as autism practitioners, we also need to know how to support the reduction of stress and anxiety that people with autism all too often live with.

Becoming autism aware

When you begin working in any kind of residential or supported living service for people with a learning disability, one of your first tasks will be to read through information contained in the files for that person. These will hopefully include a good support plan or person centred plan as well as other documents. It is here that you may first come across the word 'autism' associated with certain people. It is possible that as a new member of staff part of your induction and initial training will include a session on understanding autism. For many I know this is likely to be an e-learning module or face to face training with a trainer who has some experience and can share their knowledge to give you that all important 'awareness.'

Then you begin work and if any of the e-learning or training stays with you it is likely to only be a small amount. So you are aware that autism exists, you are aware that one or more of the people you are working with has autism, but what often does not happen is that you are told you may need to work in different ways with someone with autism.

During a home visit recently, I met Joe, a relatively new support worker. I had been asked to go as there were some concerns about a young man called Chris who spent quite a lot of time in his room, but recently he was even asking to have meals in his room. Joe had been asked to talk to me and tell me a bit about Chris and then introduce me to him. Joe explained in the following way:

> *"Chris likes to be on his own a lot and do his own thing. He loves watching all the old videos he has like Dad's Army and Open All Hours. He also likes to look at his train books and sometimes we go down to the railway station and watch the trains. I think it is because he has autism and they like things to stay the same don't they? Quite why he is asking to have his meals in his room we aren't sure. Sometimes I can get him to come down and I feel he is ok. We just have to accept him for who he is don't we? Offer him the choices, try to persuade him, but then it has got to be up to him."*

Joe is aware of Chris's autism and he is also aware that change can be difficult for people with autism, but does that knowledge impact on the way he offers support? My answer would be no. He is just using persuasion and encouragement in a very neurotypical way with phrases like, *"Go on, you will enjoy being with the others"* or *"Just come down and sit with me, we can eat together, go on."*

As is so often the case, I can hear the voice of many able people with autism as I try to explain a little more about autism to Joe. Remember John Simpson's cry of, *"What's in it for me?"* (Hatton and Simpson, 2012). Motivation is key, but to grasp how to best motivate someone with autism requires a little more knowledge and understanding than just noting the information in their file or on their person centred plan. Chris needs a motivator that really means something to him and it could well be something that may seem strange if you do not understand autism or Chris very well.

Choice and control the autism friendly way

Chris likes trains was one of the first things I was told so could this be used in some way as a motivator? Could a trip to the station happen after lunch with Joe? Could Joe bring in some postcards of trains and work on creating a scrapbook with Joe by having lunch together and then sticking the cards in the scrapbook and looking at the pictures that are already there? This may not sound very exciting to many people, but for Chris it could be just the autism friendly way of working that he needs in order to support him to be a little more sociable and spend time with people. Social time that is motivated by the things Chris likes.

I believe it is important to support and encourage social time even with those who express the desire to spend most of their time alone. Being with others for some time each day aids both social and emotional development, two key areas that with a little more knowledge about autism we would know they need support with.

The concept of being more autism friendly is introduced to Joe and a suggestion that he does an additional day's training to develop his knowledge. Joe is keen to get things right for Chris and so agrees to do this and takes on board the ideas about trains. Before long, Joe is working in a more autism friendly way and he discovers there is a narrow gauge steam railway just 20 miles away that Joe has not visited since he came to live in his current home over three years ago. A trip is planned to the railway and photos are taken and added to the scrapbook and Joe continues to use trains as a motivator in different ways to involve Chris in the life of the house.

Autism awareness has moved to an autism friendly way of working. You just need to remember that not all people with autism love trains. When some support is needed for Daniel who lives in the same house as Chris and is only motivated by string and is currently being quite destructive in the house, that ability to work in an autism friendly way needs to be adapted in order for effective support to be offered to Daniel.

Autism friendly ways of working

Perhaps the most important step to becoming autism friendly is to be aware of the things that interest and capture the attention of the people with autism we work with or are introduced to. It is one of the first things I ask, so that when I meet someone for the first time I seek to make myself of interest or of value to them by either holding or wearing something that is a part of their special interest.

We used to talk more about obsessions in autism and thankfully this has moved on as we become more aware. It may appear like an obsession but often it is just an intense area of interest that brings joy and satisfaction when immersed in it.

In the last two years, I have gone to meet someone carrying an Apple computer having been told their main area of interest was in Apple products. The young man concerned spotted the computer almost before he saw me and it was an immediate point of contact. I know he wasn't that interested in me but I gave myself the best chance at getting to know him by holding in my hand a key motivator. I was trying to behave in an autism friendly way.

There have been two occasions when trying to make myself of interest or of value to a person with autism has involved me making a simple dress from a duvet cover that has the right pictures on it. The first time it was Postman Pat and the second time it was covered in rabbits. For those who have limited spoken language, I have wanted to try and make myself of visual interest without the need for any words or holding a particular object in my hand. This method of being autism friendly has worked on both occasions and I have been accepted. At this point of acceptance, I am then able to just observe or engage and seek a deeper understanding of the person who may love Postman Pat, but refuse to have anything else in their bedroom, including a bed.

Knowing that change is difficult and being prepared to give people warning of changes that will happen, or having a plan B that is very similar to plan A, so that stress and anxiety are not made worse is also autism friendly. Many staff I meet are working in autism friendly ways and they are able to do this because of an increased level of training which informs practice. Sometimes it does seem to come naturally and intuitively with a member of staff but in my experience that is rare, though it does happen. The more normal way to autism friendly practice is through a real interest on the part of the staff member that has led them to learn more and seek out further training.

Jenny is a senior support worker in a residential service for 15 men who have a learning disability, a mental health condition or have autism. She was aware of autism and she really wanted to support the men she worked with better. Jenny attended a more detailed autism course and began to increase her knowledge and understanding. She read more, researched on the internet and began creating autism profiles for all the men in the service where she worked who had a diagnosis or significant autism traits that would warrant a diagnosis. The more she learnt and applied her knowledge, the more autism friendly her working practice has become.

The sensory needs of people are being acknowledged and addressed, special interests are engaged with and the creation of the autism profiles really helps to keep the autism in mind and see how differently it can impact for different people. She is also able to see how having choice can be just too stressful at times for some of those she works with and is not afraid to make a decision for them despite some opposition from colleagues. Jenny is confident enough in her own knowledge to be able to explain and even defend her decision to make a choice for someone. But it does not stop there of course. Once the person is calmer and less anxious, choice can be offered or encouraged and in fact should be in order to avoid people being left in their rooms on the pretext that they are choosing to be on their own all the time.

One member of staff working in an informed autism friendly way has really had an impact and people's lives are changing. This is wonderful to see and for me is clear evidence of the value of the level of training that Jenny attended. It was an undergraduate certificate in autism that included six days face to face learning as well as assignments that were work based and linked with her role at the residential home. With this increased level of knowledge, her ability to work flexibly in autism friendly ways with various residents was impressive.

As a senior support worker, her role is very much to lead the shift and tell the other staff what to do and who to be with each day. She had found she was in the office, sorting petty cash, dealing with appointments and talking on the phone. The need for her to lead by example while directly supporting the people within the service came as a result of the higher level of training described above that was concentrated and embedded in practice. Jenny returned to the workplace after each two day training enthused with new insights and ready to try new ways of working, more autism friendly ways.

The step to working in a truly autism intelligent way came when faced with difficulties she couldn't seem to work out. In this situation, she did not just go with her own ideas but tried hard to 'think autism.' Revisiting the autism profiles, seeking the ideas from the people themselves and her colleagues to flesh out those profiles to give a broader picture of the way autism impacts for each person. So often we try to solve problems using our own neurotypical way of thinking and what we need to do is very different if we are to be able to work in autism intelligent ways.

Working in an autism intelligent way

A small staff team has been working with Stephen who has autism combined with some mental health issues that have developed over the years, due at least in part to people not always working with him in autism friendly ways. I first became involved because of a crisis in Stephen's life and his admission to a psychiatric ward due to the deterioration of his mental health. I spoke at length with the senior support worker from Stephen's supported living service who I felt had some very autism friendly ideas but seemed afraid to execute them. He was keen to develop and really engage with Stephen's special interests but felt that spending time building models and playing with a train set might not be seen as work. But this was the essence of making Stephen feel at ease and so once discharged from hospital the small staff team set about 'thinking autism' in everything they did with Stephen.

Stephen's life did seem quite restricted as his choice making was limited, but by supporting him with his special interests the team found they were able to offer suggestions and the train layout became a town that incorporated an airport and a drive in cinema. Model building became part of most shifts as staff discovered that sitting on the floor in one of the rooms in Stephen's house fixing lights for the runway of his model airport really was work and was an effective way of supporting Stephen to develop his interests and make new choices.

Stephen likes to walk to places, so staff have stopped being concerned about how long it takes in a day to complete a simple task like paying the bills and have incorporated a five mile round trip on foot that also includes a favourite café for hot chocolate. This has developed over time into exploring different cafés in the city and sampling their hot chocolate and then inviting the manager from his support service to come and experience the one Stephen has decided is the best hot chocolate. Stephen has enjoyed this process and has made choices and decisions that would not have been thought possible.

Stephen's love of hot chocolate has developed in a similar way to the expansion of his model train layout, by staff thinking from within Stephen's world and suggesting a possible next step. Waffles are a speciality in some of the cafés that they visit with Stephen for hot chocolate and so the hunt for the best waffle began and when a really good one was found the manager from his service and several others were invited to see what they thought about the waffles.

You might be thinking how unhealthy all these sweet things are and of course you are right, but if you have walked a few miles to get there at a brisk pace and the intention is to walk back it is not quite so unhealthy and in fact Stephen is fit and not overweight. Slowly, but in a very autism intelligent way, the staff team have enabled Stephen to increase his choices and to make decisions about his day. They have expanded his horizons from the models in his flat to transport in different cities, from hot chocolate at one particular café to waffles and cupcake makers across a large city. The staff have attended training courses on autism and worked with Stephen on his own autism profile, recognising the key part stress and anxiety can play in his life, particularly if the staff supporting him are not autism aware, autism friendly and able to work in autism intelligent ways.

At times this has led to conflict with other professionals, but with support this staff team have been able to see that the way they have developed is good for Stephen's wellbeing. It has been a journey that has included so much more than what I have been able to describe so far and one that has been questioned and challenged but eventually acknowledged as a good way of working for Stephen's mental health, precisely because it is an autism intelligent way of working.

Stephen can often wake in the morning in an agitated state. He is able to talk about it most of the time, but talking did not seem to help. In fact it appeared to distress him more. The manager came up with an idea, what I would call a truly autism intelligent idea, as she recognised that often his dreams and negative early morning thoughts could so easily ruin a day for Stephen and they needed to be dealt with, but in a way that worked for him. Two folders were created, one dark green and one light green – colour choices from Stephen. The dark green folder was for staff to write down any positive dreams or thoughts Stephen had in a morning and the light green one was for the staff to write down his negative thoughts and dreams. Once written in the folders, the next step was for staff to send an email to the manager with any negative thoughts or dreams so that they could be sent away. The positive ones just remained in the dark green folder and Stephen was happy with this. The manager would acknowledge these emails with a simple statement. *"Thank you, I have received the email and now Stephen can get on with his day."* With the negative thoughts and dreams being sent away, Stephen feels ready and able to get on with his day and make choices about the route to be taken to a particular café or the next building project in his model city.

There are those who think that his negative thoughts must be coming from somewhere and they should be explored in order to be dealt with. The reality for Stephen is quite different. He has autism and for him to be able to see those negative and distressing ideas go into a light green folder and then on to an email and sent away has really helped him to enjoy life and move forward. It has enabled him to develop his ability to make choices and decisions, yes within a limited sphere of interest but this is an ongoing journey for Stephen and the staff who work with him. The key factor for success has been to 'think autism' and to think Stephen's autism, getting to know him and supporting him in an autism intelligent way to flourish and be able to make choices but choices that do not cause stress and anxiety as they start from within the things that are special to Stephen.

I recommend that when you work with people with autism you first of all have to be autism aware and this should bring your attention to any difficulties around choice and decision making. As a member of staff supporting someone with autism there will, I believe, be times when you need to both restrict choice and make decisions for that person if they are to be able to get through a stressful day.

There will also be times when to work in an autism friendly manner you need to make suggestions and offer a limited choice but rooted in their sphere of interest. You will always need to be thinking carefully around issues of choice in order to ensure those you support are not anxious or stressed by the fact there are three cereals on the table for breakfast and that for them on this occasion this is just too much and could seriously ruin their day.

When it comes to involving someone in making choices and decisions about their future, even just talking about it can cause stress. However, if you support them to know there will be some definite and very predictable things in their future and if you enable them to really see and experience the kinds of choices you are talking about, it will be possible for them to make a truly 'informed' choice. This will not happen easily, it takes time and autism intelligent thinking but it is possible and it is what we should be aiming for. I hope very much that this book will have helped you to see it is a little more complicated than just saying, *"Well, it is his choice, he is an adult now and is able to make his own choices."*

Perhaps a phrase that John Simpson (Hatton and Simpson, 2012) often uses is the best quote to end with to keep us 'thinking autism.' John says, for him as an autistic person, *"Autism is the quest for predictability"*. This has got to make us think differently about how we support and develop the ability to make choices and decisions for people with autism.

References

Attwood, T (2008) *The Complete Guide to Asperger Syndrome*. London: Jessica Kingsley Publishers

Baron-Cohen (1995) *Mindblindess: An essay on autism and theory of mind*. London: MIT Press

Brown, H and Smith, H (eds) (1992) *Normalisation: A reader*. Abingdon: Routledge

Caldwell, P (2005) *Finding You Finding Me: Using intensive interaction to get in touch with people whose severe learning disabilities are combined with autistic spectrum disorder*. London: Jessica Kingsley Publishers

Caldwell, P (2007) *Learning the Language. Building relationships with people with severe learning disability, autistic spectrum disorder and other challenging behaviours* (DVD). Hove: Pavilion Publishing

Caldwell, P (2010) *Autism and Intensive Interaction* (DVD). London: Jessica Kingsley Publishers

Department of Health (1971) *Better Services for the Mentally Handicapped*. London: HMSO

Department of Health (2001) *Valuing People: A new strategy for learning disability for the 21st Century*. London: Department of Health

Department of Health (2009) *Valuing People Now: A new three year strategy for people with learning disabilities*. London: Department of Health

Department of Health (2010) *Fulfilling and Rewarding Lives: The strategy for adults with autism in England*. London: Department of Health

Department of Health (2014) *Think Autism. Fulfilling and Rewarding Lives, The Strategy for Adults with Autism in England: An update*. London: Department of Health

Grace Baron, M, Groden, J, Groden, G and Lipsitt, L P (2006) *Stress and Coping in Autism*. Oxford: Oxford University Press

Grandin, T and Johnson, C (2009) *Animals Make Us Human. Creating the best life for animals*. New York: Houghton-Mifflin Harcourt

Hatton, S and Boughton, T (2011) *An Introduction to Supporting People with Autistic Spectrum Conditions*. Birmingham: BILD

Hatton, S and Simpson, J (2012) *Next Steps in Supporting People with Autistic Spectrum Conditions*. Birmingham: BILD

Hatton, S (2015) Supporting staff to 'Think Autism' through the regular use of individual autism profiles. *Good Autism Practice*, 16, 1, 42-52

Hewett, D, Barber, M, Firth, G and Harrison, T (2011) *The Intensive Interaction Handbook*. London: Sage Publications

Kanner, L (1943) Autistic disturbances of affective contact. *The Nervous Child* 2:217–250. Reset in: Kanner, L (1973) *Childhood Psychosis: Initial studies and new insights.* New York: John Wiley & Sons

King's Fund Centre (1980) *An Ordinary Life: Comprehensive locally-based residential services for mentally handicapped people.* London: King's Fund Centre

Lawson, W (1998) *Life Behind Glass. A personal account of autism spectrum disorder.* London: Jessica Kingsley Publishers

Lawson, W (2001) *Understanding and Working with the Spectrum of Autism: An insider's view.* London: Jessica Kingsley Publishers

Mental Capacity Act 2005. Download from http://bit.ly/1LWKvyv

O'Brien, J and Lyle O'Brien, C (1988) *A Little Book About Person Centred Planning.* Toronto: Inclusion Press

Sperlinger, A (1992) Changing services. In: Brown, H and Benson, S (eds) *A Practical Guide to Working with People with Learning Disabilities. A handbook for care assistants and support workers.* London: Hawker Publications

The Education (Handicapped Children) Act 1970. Download from: http://bit.ly/1ToZv05

The Mental Deficiency Act 1913. London: HM Government

Tilly, L (2011) *Person Centred Approaches when Supporting People with a Learning Disability.* Birmingham: BILD

Towell, D (ed) (1988) *An Ordinary Life in Practice: Developing comprehensive Ccommunity-based services for people with learning disabilities.* London: King's Fund Centre

Webb, T (1992) *A is for Autism* (DVD). British Film Industry

Williams, D (1998) *Nobody Nowhere. The remarkable autobiography of an autistic girl.* London: Jessica Kingsley Publishers

Wing, L (2002) *The Autistic Spectrum. A guide for parents and professionals.* Revised edition. London: Constable & Robinson Ltd

Wolfensberger, W (2004) Social role valorization. A proposed new term for the principle of normalization. In: Mitchell, D (ed) *Special Educational Needs and Inclusive Education. Major themes in education. Volume I, systems and contexts.* London: RoutledgeFalmer